In Bed with the Cats' Pyjamas

Poems by Dick Dixon

Drawings by Reine Mazoyer

Mereo Books

2nd Floor, 6-8 Dyer Street, Cirencester, Gloucestershire, GL7 2PF
An imprint of Memoirs Books. www.mereobooks.com
and www.memoirsbooks.co.uk

In Bed with the Cats' Pyjamas
978-1-86151-808-8

First published in Great Britain in 2022

© Poems - Dick Dixon
© Illustrations - Reine Mazoyer

Copyright ©2022

Dick Dixon has asserted his right under the Copyright Designs and
Patents Act 1988 to be identified as the author of this work.

Reine Mazoyer asserts her right to be identified as the author of the illustrations.

The address for Memoirs Books can be
found at www.mereobooks.com

Mereo Books Ltd. Reg. No. 12157152

Contents

Preface

Welcome everyone, to the world of illustrated humorous (or possibly philosophical) poetry. The current book is the fourth in a series that began with 'Rhymes for no Reason', continuing with 'Rhymes of the Newfangled Mariner' and 'The Curse of the Square Crow'.

We are aiming to continue a tradition of such writing, which seems to be in danger in this strange new world of digital downloads and Bluetooth, of dying the most undignified death of a thousand or so cuts.

The solution of course is to breathe new life into the stricken patient by the simple means of ink, paint and paper. In an even older tradition, it might have been 'stone, scissors and paper', but alas that does not usually result in a book.

It would be a shame, surely, not to be able to read about a new kind of umbrella that can help you to make a cup of tea in a completely original and unexpected way, at the same time saving on your water bills – or how to settle the question of whether you are really a divine being, presumably in disguise, and no matter what your other half has to say on the subject. On the other hand, we reveal the little-known secret of baby beets, which are so often discovered languishing in jars in a supermarket setting; they come to us by a very strange process indeed, which is presented here for the very first time I would imagine. I doubt whether this kind of revelation is likely to find its way to the Sunday papers, but surely it must be a close-run thing.

Have you heard the strange story of the vicar of Stiffkey, and how he managed to depart this earth at the hands (or perhaps paws, or even jaws) of a lioness? It is a small, but amazing part of the story of our lives in these islands.

There again, did you realise how important the humble doorknob is in the diagnosis of disease in our doctors' surgeries? I do regret having to 'spill the beans' on this one, but it had to be done I think. In any case, this phenomenon has been recognised as important from the early days of medicine, for example Doctor Finlay, or at least since we had knobs on our doors! Handles are also good, but do not have quite the same magical aura of course.

I must just mention a final thing of some importance: how to rid your bedroom of mosquitoes in the summer; surely nobody wishes to be plagued with these rotten insects. The solution to this may involve a trip to Tibet, but it will be well worth the effort, as you will see. You will not see this on a comparison website, I promise!

There are many other curious situations and ideas described in the thirty-three poems, each of which has its own illustration in full colour by the well-known brilliant French artist Reine Mazoyer – and for those people whose native language is French, we have, as in 'The Curse of the Square Crow', provided French explanations of the poems, towards the end of the book.

We wish you a happy time as you grapple with some of the strangenesses of our lives today – or was it yesterday?

Dick Dixon
December 2021

In Bed with the Cats' Pyjamas

Congratulations

Weddings are such lovesome things,
With feasting, priest and pretty rings;
The congregation hope and pray,
And press to bless your wedding day.
Bouquets, confetti fill the air,
Then – consummation on a creaky stair!

Abiding joy a new child is:
Champagne, Prosecco – any fizz
Will do to wet the baby's head,
And say 'well done' to Fran and Fred,
For they and theirs have yet again
Forged one more link in the human chain.

A golden wedding's rather fun;
Amazing how fleet time has run,
Or rather flown with fifty wings,
With fifty years of naughty flings –
And pots of gold at rainbow's end,
With cake and kisses from old friends.

A funeral is sad indeed –
Our prayers will help to say 'Godspeed';
A wooden rocket ship awaits
The journey to the pearly gates,
While we stand by in tearful state –
No need at last to congratulate!

The Cats' Pyjamas

Black shadows stretch across the land –
Jagged, cold and long,
And silence stirs from slumber,
To sing its sombre song;
Just cast a misted eye around,
Whirl round and through, towards the dark,
A swirling gown of blue that drowns –
And grasp the grass that was the park.

With darkness there comes magic;
The stars and moon stare down –
And are they caught in the rictus
Of a strangely tortured frown?
All is oddly altered now,
To a dream-like state, and yet
The wind in whispers tells of how
And why this surreal stage was set.

Atop a twisted sycamore
Or beside a winding stair,
They come to sit in moonlight –
You won't believe they're there;
They flicker, glow in blue half-light,
And sit in waiting facing west,
For though all's now in steep of night,
The red sun died there as it set.

In unison, a song of praise
These felines meet in hope to give
Their thanks to our vermilion sun,
That it might once more rise and live
Next day, its light to shine and show
The way to rest on sills and floors –
As wise with whiskers, heaven knows,
In daytime cats prefer indoors.

As night arrives they're summoned forth,
Assembling in the hallowed air;
When hunting creatures of the dark,
They first miaow a fervent prayer:
Echoes in a celestial hall,
A caterwaul from earth to sky –
An urgent and insistent call,
And a terror to the passer-by.

And lest they risk that light of day
Might never shine on earth again,
Dressed head to paw they serenade
Their vanished globe, and hope retain;
In clothes befitting every one,
And versed so well in laws of karma,
Defers each one to the sunken sun –
In a suit of pink pyjamas.

*According to one of the perhaps less well-known laws of karma, it is always
preferable to acknowledge deference to the object of one's adoration
in a muted form, lest it be misinterpreted as a wish to upstage or outdo
that object. Hence the wise choice of pink pyjamas, rather than a garish red
or orange. This demonstrates accord in a subtle way, it is recorded.*

Mysteries

I cannot really tell you
Why the sun sets in the west,
Or if the holes need washing
In a very old string vest.

But I can solve some mysteries
About some other things:
For example, how brave hedgehogs
Make love when comes each spring.

And why a bicycle's so hard
To mount before your ride,
If you choose to try your ascent
From its surly right-hand side.

Also, have you wondered why
The moon floats upside down,
When seen by wombats in a wood,
Or dingoes out of town?

And then there's holy water,
I'll show you how to spout –
Divining water from the tap,
Then boiling hell right out!

I recall though that I've wondered
About my mortal state:
Whether there's a mystery there,
And whether it is fate.

The question is of purpose,
And why we're really here –
And is my heart reliable
To say which course to steer?

I should perhaps be honest –
And define my beating heart,
By telling of its musings –
The mystique of its art.

At times it's 'doki-doki',
When Tokyo is near,
But then it's 'doogan-doogan',
When home is far Korea.

It says, it seems quite clearly,
All that needs be said –
Of life and love and yearning:
How yet they might be wed.

But all around this errant world,
A thousand versions play,
Their voices named as various,
That speak no common way.

So always and forever,
No puzzle that persists,
Is why my love's not steadfast,
Nor grows while it exists.

The Island

No man is an island,
Or so the poet said,
But did he really ever move
Far from his restful bed?
We know he was in London,
And at Oxford too he read,
And continental Europe
Did bear his earthly tread.

But really John, if only
You'd ventured north instead,
You would have found a counter
To right your errant head;
It's true it's cold and rainy,
In northern climes for sure –
But we must labour for the truth,
Or suffer all the more.

Four horses and a carriage,
Were all you needed, see?
No cause for desperation –
Just oats and bread and Brie.
Perhaps you had no inkling,
'Twas where salvation lay:
A shining golden island,
Where tailless cats did play.

Ah, but now I see it –
Of course – a blinding light!
If you'd ever journeyed there,
Your line you'd never write;
You must have sensed that somehow,
You had to keep away –
Or drown in that dilemma,
About just what to say.

And so we kept your poem,
No man can deny it,
Nor need to ask the bell for whom
It tolls – nor need divine it;
Perhaps a dream foretold this,
That you had to stay your hand;
Great thanks in any case you found
No route to the Isle of Man.

Powder Theory

I have kept my powder dry,
In case of indigestion,
But that has never helped me try
To answer other questions.

Better would have been to wet
It every now and then,
When indigestion was no threat,
To see what hidden friend
I might have had for all that wasted time:
To find if things I'd missed
While bathing idly in the prime
Of life, might strike me with a kiss.

'Too late now', I hear you say;
The hours cannot adjust their tack,
And indigestion never came my way.
Perhaps I should just go and hit the sack.

My Goat

If you walk across the park,
You'll never find my goat;
He's just not there, so please don't stare,
And don't put on your coat.

You'll think maybe – there's little doubt,
He's over by the shed;
But can you see him, honestly,
With that horned and bearded head?

Not yours of course; he is the one
I speak of in this case –
Though to him I see resemblances
In your Capricorn goat face.

But if only you could see him,
With his perfect white coiffed coat,
His head held at an angle,
To reveal his noble throat.

He's wise, and so intelligent,
And plays the lute it's said,
Especially as the sun retreats,
To rest its weary head.

Well, is he on the green back lawn?
It's true the grass is short;
No, my goat's not responsible –
He's simply not the sort.

My goat's a little fussy,
Though it's true he dines for free;
But mere grass is so pedestrian,
And also walked upon, you see.

My goat is upper echelon,
Or middle class at least;
He doesn't mix with lesser goats –
This condescending beast!

My goat's always vigilant,
For a chance at something more;
His palate's quite exquisite –
Sometimes caviar's a bore!

He's also fond of vintage wine,
At least that is the talk –
It's lucky though he struggles
With removal of the cork!

He'll sneak into the kitchen,
When the fridge door's open wide –
And remove the lovely truffles
That I've hidden deep inside.

I don't think I can take much more,
I've made a mental note;
If only I could find him –
It really gets my goat.

Stand Clear

Stand clear – of the blast
From the reddening sky,
As the world at last
Wakes hearts and minds
Of the dead and the blind –
To repent this day,
As the time is spent
And darkness is nigh;

Too late is the cry
From the bed of the earth –
Though the sun gave light,
Soon will be night,
And the moon, so near,
Draws wave upon wave
Over meadow and grave;
So run for the river
That drowns or saves,
Though the wood's in flame,
And the birds take wing
For the moonlit shore.

Don't blame or berate –
It's much too late;
No claim, no point,
No date – it's now;
Your fate – it's here;
Wake up, or fall
You must, to dust –
That's all.
Stand clear!

A Leap In The Dark

If you're fast asleep,
Then: 'Look before you leap!'
Seems excellent advice,
You must admit.
For jumping in the dark
In garden, pool or park,
Is simply asking for
A problem caused by it.

Somnambulistic sport
Is particularly fraught,
For reasons which I'm sure
Will be quite plain,
So if this case I take –
Well, it's better you're awake!
At least you'll have a chance
To miss the pain.

After all, you may arrive
At the far end of your dive,
In a ditch or dyke that's dug
With love and pride –
By a man with sharpened spade,
Who may launch a blue tirade,
Especially if he's still
Around inside!

And that's not all I fear,
As a sharpened spade it's clear
Can cause pain quite severe
In ditch or dyke;
Much wiser to think twice,
As it really isn't nice
To lose a body part
You rather like!

To sum up my suspicion:
A change of disposition
Would really be advised
In terms of cost;
'Look before you leap!'
Is much safer than to sleep –
Though take note that he who
Hesitates is lost.

The Bees' Knees

There is no doubt – or so it's said,
That bees have tiny knees;
They may not know, nor even care,
When buzzing through the shining air –
But let's not seem to stand and stare
From underneath the trees.

Binoculars may penetrate
This mystery soon enough:
These humans with extended eyes –
The bees will think us mad, not wise!
But we are mad keen for the prize,
And peer like crazy from the rough.

It's in the paper – black and white;
They really want to know,
Whether bees have knees or not,
And if it's true, their function's – what?
More than likely though, it's rot,
A so-called fact that isn't so.

Carnations, roses – poppies too:
Their scent hangs by the threads
Of gold that shimmer like a wave –
Pulsating essence they all crave,
That makes them delve and makes them brave
To echo blueprints in their heads.

Now they're at the hollyhocks,
In deep engagement there,
Their steady buzzing all around –
A quintessential summer sound,
While lazy clouds survey the ground
From far above, in cooler air.

Each prying lens can pick them out,
These busy black-legged bees –
They enter through prismatic glass,
To avaricious eyes and gasp,
And all agog that now at last
May yield – the secret of the knees!

But look now, as they rise as one –
Pollen-laden as they are,
And form a circle by the path,
Their merry buzz almost a laugh,
Its pitch now risen by a half –
At least it sounds so from afar.

The circle by the path expands,
Around a central core,
And at its centre there's a hum
Beneath the ground – a high-pitched drum;
An eerie sound that seems to come
From way below the earthen floor.

Then in time the centre melts –
And in each lens reflects;
Each head is bowed, each abdomen
Raised as though to write – a pen
To scribe the summer sky, and then –
The bees as one now genuflect.

Risen up, in golden light,
A vision, never seen by men,
So splendid in the setting sun,
The archetype of every one –
In admiration finely spun,
And maybe never seen again.

Melissa, goddess of the bees
Appears before her acolytes;
A gleaming beauty, now she's seen –
Pulsing silver, gold and green,
Wings delicately traced, she preens;
Never was there such a sight.

In adoration, bees prepare
A buzzing chorus now:
Their heads are level, I can see,
And from their wings, in key of B,
A hymn of praise, with melody;
Melissa gives a heartfelt bow.

But consternation clouds my mind –
It now occurs to me,
That even though we're all inspired,
Some evidence will be required;
I really hope I won't be fired,
Or sent post-haste to Coventry!

I've spoken to the editor;
His knitted brow confirms
That everything I said, he heard:
"Such arrant nonsense, every word" –
He'd rather hear of ten-foot birds
That live on purple snails and worms!

Or failing that, he says he'd like
To own a pack of llamas –
To study in his leisure time,
And that's not all – it's such a crime:
The thing to him that's most sublime?
Why cats wear pink pyjamas!

*Readers may like to note that all this occurred long before
the advent of the smartphone, and the 'office camera' was
on loan that day.   Hell, it was only supposed to be a
preliminary investigation! What can you do? The moral of
the story must be that one must be prepared for the
unexpected at all times.*

Doorknob Revelations

A doorknob passes, in disguise –
A shiny, secret, silent bomb,
Unnoticed on its door, I'd say;
A commonplace, there every day,
But in plain sight and come what may,
Performs all week with such aplomb.

Its mesmerising presence felt
In morning rooms that chill the blood;
A talisman, physician's friend
That watches patiently, and when
Consulting time is at an end,
Extracts bald truth – we knew it would.

No snake oil, nor Pentothal
Is needed here at all you see –
First a rush of trivial complaints:
Woes come forth of frights and faints,
But the doctor does no harm, and waits –
And lends some well-worn sympathy.

And then to follow, pleasant chat,
After which a chair-leg scrapes,
Then – dead-legged journey in a trance;
Oh well – regret – the only chance
Recedes, and early fears advance
Again – such pitiful escape.

But no, the hand is on the door;
The doorknob turns – grates in its tracks;
It seems a jolt of current stabs –
Gives courage to reveal the scabs,
Or horrid pox or spots, and grabs
From quaking inner parts the facts.

The doc bestows his knowing smile;
He's tramped this path a thousand fold:
'Oh doctor, what on earth to do?
I can't sleep – it's guilt for you;
Let sins be told: I'm seeing Sue,
You know, your wife – she's good as gold!'

The 'doorknob revelation' is I believe a phenomenon well-known to the medical profession. The main problem here is that there is no guarantee regarding the precise nature of the revelation. This fact, and sometimes the revelation itself, can occasionally cause a little consternation.

A Midnight Feast

One day in spring when youth was mine,
I scanned a spinning globe;
In far Tibet I placed my trust,
To solve my problem – as needs must,
In the eye of the saffron-yellow robe.

So then I journeyed day and night,
To reach this hallowed land;
With red-hot steps now far from fleet,
Was met by monks in noonday heat –
Who seemed to sense the grim intent I had.

They heard my story – hard to tell,
And craned to read my mind;
These noble men, without demur,
Conveyed their thoughts without a word –
To show their mental strength and love divine.

At sunset they would gasp and screech –
Across their room they flew;
In arcs they wheeled and often swooped,
Rose and dived with snorts and whoops,
All powered by mind and steaming lentil stew.

In time they trusted me to learn
Their truly arcane ways,
Until I could perform at will,
Manoeuvres that would make you ill,
Or at the very least I'd say, amazed.

Returning home with some regret,
Yet full of wisdom gained,
I knew at once my years of toil
Would spare me greatly midnight oil
I would have used to banish so much pain.

What do I mean? I will explain:
Hot summers bring their hordes
Of flies, mosquitoes and the rest
Of nature's winged and buzzing pests –
To my bedroom in the cool of eve, indoors.

And if I ever wish to sleep,
The buzz I must curtail,
Or rise next day with reddened skin,
Just where mosquitoes put their stings –
It's sad that there's not yet 'mosquito jail'!

But now the answer is at hand:
I take revenge that's bold –
I open wide and cruise the air,
And swallow all the insects there,
And then, with stomach full, sweet sleep enfolds.

Men You Must Meet

Plumbers will turn on
The waterworks when
You tell them you can't
Ever see them again.

Lawyers will tell you
To be oh so brief,
Or some bodily harm
Will bring you to grief.

Doctors will fill up
Your spaces with pills –
And probe in the darkness
To 'check you for ills'.

Teachers will say that
They're just marking time,
Unless it's a quickie
You have on your mind.

Salesmen will pester –
To check what they've got,
As if that could ever
Encourage the hots!

Cab drivers say that
They'll go all the way,
But if it's at midnight,
It's double you'll pay.

Vets are just animals
Released from a cage,
And if you don't stroke them,
It may cause a rage.

Electricians have contacts
And love to plug in,
But sparks may well fly
When you're sampling sweet sin!

Plasterers know how
To smooth it for sure:
Quick dips in the bucket,
And then back for more!

Bank robbers tell you:
'Hands in the air!'
Then go through your drawers,
To see what's in there.

It does make you think that
You're on the wrong track,
If the working man sends you
Twice to hell and then back.

Perhaps it is best to
Disdain this wild mob,
And select at your leisure
A gent with no job!

By the way – I hope you don't think that I regard
bank-robbing as a job. Heaven help us all if it were!

The Reasons

I must tell you the reasons –
I'd sing them if I could;
They'd sound their best in A flat,
Or at least be very good.

But there's a major problem
It pains me so to say,
Also one that's minor –
For later, if I may.

The fact is that the reasons
Can never come to light –
As I feel I must present them
In a way that's best and right.

And sadly I must tell you
That I cannot sing a note;
So forget the A flat notion –
It would hardly float our boat!

So that leaves A flat minor,
A noble key indeed,
But yet again we're hamstrung,
As my singing's gone to seed.

I know what you are thinking –
I think the same, it's true:
We need an old piano,
And a handy coal mine too.

But even if we had them,
It wouldn't help my voice,
The reasons would remain untold,
No cause then to rejoice.

And sorry, no use anyway,
My conscience won't permit
Your drastic, deadly answer –
I could never hear of it.

I can see that a piano,
Positioned at the mouth
Of a mine can drop in splendour,
As it goes both west and south.

Success though would mean sadness,
And frankly nothing finer,
When the huge and heavy crashing hulk –
Squeezed out A flat minor.

Time

Time will tell,
But does not
Speak your fate;
In fact, you'll
Very simply
Have to wait.

And if you thought
You could avoid this state –
Wonder, watch,
But – too late,
As someone stoops
Ahead of you,
To shut the gate.

Heavenly Gold

If your legs are ancient sticks,
And your body's going west,
With grey-topped head and floppy arms to wave,
There's one thing you'll remember,
From December to November,
About which Britons always rush to rave.

If your legs are springy though,
In grand galumphing youth,
With striding step and staring eyes aloof,
I expect you're out there walking,
And very likely talking,
About this very thing – it's just the truth.

The thing I'm hesitating
To bring up is – the rain:
The curse and blessing all of us so hate;
In Great Britain it's a mission
To avoid this wet condition –
The rain is not why Britain is so great!

We do have our umbrellas,
To shake at darkened skies,
Though rain gods may not answer to our cries;
We can brandish them, but find
That our warrant has been signed –
Then the wetness cuts our case right down to size.

But when they're up, they're up,
As the Grand Old Duke has said –
Though he was busy marching with his horde;
So we do have some protection
Against this damp infection,
But really there's much more to take on board.

What I'm saying I suppose,
Is their shape – there lies a doubt:
I wonder if convention we should flout,
As they're not quite fit for purpose –
A bit 'ex-army surplus',
When winds are strong and blow them inside out.

And the water from above,
That drips from rain-soaked clouds?
We do stay dry, but still can help our earth;
How sad that water's wasted,
And never even tasted;
How much is such a brolly really worth?

We should strive to find a way,
To respect the giving sky –
Returning thanks, with long regarding sigh;
Global warming's on the prowl
And by fair means or by foul,
We must save our water and as well keep dry.

The brolly of the future,
As yet unknown to science –
Will reform our early views upon our rain;
It'll likely save the world,
When it's gloriously unfurled –
Instead of showering rain on Spanish plains!

Ah yes, perhaps you see it,
And you think it's just a crime?
Not really, as it's here and just in time:
Inversion was the answer,
For surgeon, sweep or dancer,
Though water will be theirs, not gin and lime!

I also must make mention,
That the omnipresent rain,
Turns into liquid gold when safely trapped;
It's as soft as feather down
And as clear as Jura sound –
Much better than the junk from kitchen taps.

And in case there's still a doubt,
You'll be very glad to see –
And I think this really is the clinching key:
At the vertex there's a tap
Where the water – you extract,
So you can make the perfect cup of tea.

I feel I must be completely honest here in saying that I do doubt whether the perfect cup of tea is to be found using rainwater. However, I dare say that some people would like it.

Unholy Estate

The top-floor tenant paced his flat;
His soles in torment trod the boards.
Consumed he was with doubt and fear,
His resolution never near –
Until one day sweet silence fell,
Whereupon my shaken spirit soared.

The answer to his question lay
Beyond the mountain tops in snow,
In places witnessed not by man,
At times no clock could ever span,
Sequestered in another realm,
Yet surely – either yes or no!

Determined to resolve the case,
He summoned up a gas balloon,
With basket and a length of rope;
Up he travelled, flushed with hope,
Till far beyond the crumbs of white,
He spied a bulging harvest moon.

His neighbours saw the strange affair,
With rope that vanished in the blue –
And synchronised a steady pull,
To bring him safely back in full,
Rather than leave parts behind,
That might have made 'celestial stew'.

After hours of selfless toil,
With miles of rope coiled on the ground,
Balloon and basket reappeared,
And soon returned to earth, dog-eared
It's true, but that was not quite all –
For the man was nowhere to be found.

High and low we searched till morn
Broke on our fevered group at prayers –
Then a voice boomed loud and long,
From way above the skylark's song:
"The answer I have found is 'yes';
After all, I was the man upstairs".

Beets Of The Heart

Love is just a big red beet
That sits upon a plate;
It never seems to find its feet,
But sags, and sighs and waits.
A tiny tear of vinegar
Emerges from its eye,
With hope upon a twinkling star
That journey's end is nigh.

Days come in and days go out,
But the beet goes on and on;
Its red embarrassed self just pouts,
And wishes to be gone –
To find that perfect other that
Is out there without doubt,
But sitting on another plate –
Too far to see or shout.

The sadness is – beets cannot speak,
Less still shout for help
To find the thing they really seek,
Or be left on the shelf.
So sad it is – so hard to take,
To live alone and blue,
And also red, for heaven's sake,
Whatever can they do?

The beetroot fairy, so it seems,
Might place them next in line,
To meet the beetroot of their dreams,
Or forever pout and pine!
Or the chef, with sympathetic eye,
Could scoop them up with fish,
And place them neatly, with some pie,
At the centre of their dish.

Then – oh yes – they'd weep with joy,
No vinegar this time,
Just that girl and just this boy –
How totally sublime!
Alone at last, with plate so warm,
Let nature plot its course:
Love is such a primal storm,
When there's tartare sauce!

But let us not be hasty,
How little do we know;
Since all know beets are tasty –
They'd only last a mo',
When faced with those who 'dine at eight'
Who ate last hours ago;
They'd stand no chance while on the plate –
But nowhere else to go!

Though love's an ever rising tide,
They must stay as cool as steel,
To brave the pain of love denied,
Till midnight's heard to peal;
But then – when moon and stars conspire
To bring them to one plate,
(And diners snore before the fire),
They're free to conjugate!

Everyone knows about baby beets. You can probably find them in your local supermarket. How they were made though is a closely guarded secret!

Strange Times

It's like a furnace in Farnborough,
And they're dreadfully worried in Bude;
It's not so grand on the Isle of Man,
And in Peckham they're all in the nude!

They're drenched in Market Harborough,
But the trembling tourists on Skye
Have no idea if they're far or near,
Or whether they'll boil, bake or fry.

There's rain all right on the Isle of Wight,
But in Bedford the sun blazes down;
Even at night, there's just no respite
For those who are 'painting the town'.

They never see snow in old Glasgow,
And the streets are a riot of heat;
All the year round, no ice can be found,
And everyone's cooling their feet.

The scorching sun is not on the run,
No need for thermometers now;
It's just too hot to stir the pot,
In Bognor and Barnsley – and how!

In West Kilbride, on the Firth of Clyde,
The sun is in charge of the sea;
Watch the steam rise on the incoming tide,
Then run for your life – just like me!

In Wales, in the Gower, the sun has great power,
And the sheep are on such tenterhooks;
It's sad to relate their crystal-clear fate:
On your plate they'll be seen ready-cooked!

The wind and storms in the pretty Cairngorms
Break records as a matter of course;
Those who dwell there should not take the air,
And instead concentrate on their morse.

And it's sad to see in the Forest of Dean
That the trees are consumed in red flame;
Smoke and fire just climb higher and higher –
Who on earth could we possibly blame?

Oh what can we do? We're in a fine stew;
The climate is changing – and fast.
In fact we all know, so let us just go
And be strong – or be a thing of the past.

Safely Home

The wind is troubling now a budless bush,
While clouds of menace scud the silent dark,
And now that frosty night has spread a shroud,
The pale white crescent moon attempts her arc;
In distant woods, a dog just barks and howls,
As wailing wolves are mesmerised by owls.

Now middle earth yields up a darker side –
An entity that preys on head and heart;
And whey-faced gargoyles leer from trembling trees,
In following their own perverted art.
How long before the mind capitulates,
And calm defers, as panic strikes and starts?
If wicked spirits overcome this earth,
Do humans still have hope for safe rebirth?

That at least is how the scene appears;
The mind with ease though conjures black from white –
Will fancy not find mischief where it may,
And wrap itself in terrors of the night?
So wait: this view I saw through glass in mist,
A window of my home; it gives the key.
How truly blessed I am to be within,
And not outside where demons seem to be:
The ticking clock my heart takes for its beat,
And faithful dog in slumber at my feet –
I love the fire that warms the rose-filled room,
And Nuits-Saint-Georges to soothe me to my sleep;
The Canalettos, silver, glass and gold –
All these are wondrous comforts here to keep;
A home that's filled with music, love and light,
Is where I wish to be, please God, this night.

I thought I was immune from troubling thoughts, until
one winter's night ....

The Vicar Of Stiffkey

There he stands, a man among men,
A prince perhaps, among princes –
Of noble mind and such chaste heart,
And little over sixty inches.

To Stiffkey in north Norfolk then –
Young Harold Davidson began
In residence as vicar there,
And preached on Sundays to his fans.

And in his heart there beat a blood
So rare, so red, so pure it bled
All through his tiny frame and brain;
He tried to follow where it led.

He thought females the weaker sex
Most likely, so his way was clear:
No armour, but he'd be their knight,
To rescue them from doubt and fear.

He tramped the streets of London town,
In constant search for troubled souls
To save, and set on better lives,
Especially if attractive girls.

Such girls comprised some ladies, true,
And sometimes 'ladies of the night',
But Harold was a man of God,
Who showed them all the path of light.

Though no one had much cause to doubt
That Harold was quite genuine,
His actions caused his bishop now
To smoke his pipe and stroke his chin.

They brought him in for questioning,
Yet nothing really could they find,
But even so, I'm sad to say,
Unfrocked poor Harold – most unkind!

Trafalgar Day it was as well,
Which seemed to make things so much worse,
But Harold rallied, truth to tell,
And found a way to lift the curse.

An inward consultation brought
His thoughts towards an actor's life:
Blessed he was with thespian genes –
But little knew of pending strife.

To Blackpool then – he joined a group
Who pleased the crowds, but lived on broth;
Spectators loved to see his tricks –
And that he had been 'of the cloth'.

He wore a barrel – flirted too
With prodding from a devil's fork,
Rotated on a metal spit,
Which made it hard to walk or talk.

The fickle public soon turned tail –
So Harold crossed to Skegness now,
And joined a troupe of circus folk,
To hone his new-found craft – and how!

In a cage, two lions at rest
Watched Harold as he worked the crowd,
Outside the cage in safety now,
His words of wisdom told out loud.

Then his inner demon pressed –
To give a sermon scorning sin,
In the cage that held the lions;
The Lord would keep him safe within.

But the Lord was not prepared
To give his blessing at that time;
Toto and Freddie watched and sniffed,
As Harold pondered – thoughts sublime.

The cage he entered, full of hope,
But sadly trod on Toto's tail;
The lioness roared her clear distress,
And Freddie yawned – the silent male!

But now she had him in her mouth,
And though the tamer fought to free
Him from this onslaught hard to bear,
Poor Harold was a sight to see.

They took him to the hospital,
And tried to save his life for days;
He battled on, but could not last,
And sadly, Harold passed away.

He's buried in the churchyard now,
In old Stiffkey's village church,
How sad this hero, brave and true,
Was left so badly in the lurch!

The poem tells the sad story of Harold Davidson, the vicar of Stiffkey (pronounced locally as something like 'Stewkey'). The main events took place in the period 1932 to 1937, and gained a good deal of attention in the newspapers of the time. He was ordained originally in 1903 as an assistant curate in Westminster, but posted three years later to Stiffkey in north Norfolk, near Wells. However, it seems that he missed the bright lights of London, and in fact travelled there each Monday morning from about 1906, returning the following Saturday in time to give a Sunday sermon in Stiffkey. While in London, he would continue his mission of saving fallen women. The details are quite complex, but you can easily discover how Harold, most probably innocent of much wrongdoing, came eventually, after many years, to be unfrocked (to use the original term), and essentially betrayed by the Church of England. This led to his untimely death, aged 62, on July 30th 1937, having been mauled two days earlier by a lioness called Toto.

Vacuum Cleaning

A vacuum, as you surely know,
Is a truly simple thing;
Defined it is to be a void –
Not a parcel wrapped in string.
There's nothing there, but don't you see?
It means we surely ought to sing.

What's that you say – you just can't sing?
But I really must insist!
After all, a great advance
Has loomed up from the mist,
So don't delay, and sing hooray;
We've waited – oh so long for this.

The thing is, what's impossible
Is to make a vacuum clean –
It has no dirt, and nothing else;
Not even half a mouldy bean,
So lock away your Hoovers now –
Make whoopee on the village green!

Romance Of Selene

I watch you gazing at the clear full moon –
A sphere of shining silver in our sight;
How constant, but also gone so soon –
Now silently suspended in this night.

Constant yes, but only for a while,
Her slow decline a measure of the days:
Two weeks to pass, then gone with all her guile,
Then slow return – what does she mean to say?
Does sometimes though another facet press
To make her act in desperation's way?
Can we then sense her distant quiet distress,
When evening sky must fail to make her stay?

She then, respecting earthly bonds, conceals
Her face in the sapphire blue of day;
Is here a sign that we should gather strength,
And follow her to light, as is her way?
How easily we'd copy, you and I:
Silver moons apart a million miles,
Each haunted by such strange geometry
As constrains our shining cousin in the skies.

For a million years we humans have been told,
No wiser now than ever we were then –
We're born and live and grow, in shadows, old,
In Plato's cave, and scarcely comprehend;
We cross, we pass, we turn our faces out –
Then in, as through the daily round we're groomed,
Yet hide the truth from those who in plain sight,
Find comfort in the easily assumed.

Worlds turn the while, though hands and faces burn,
I see it in your eyes – your clear unease;
But one day soon we'll know, no longer yearn:
Our love is locked – until we find the keys.

Readers may have noticed that there are times when our moon declines to appear in the cold night sky, sometimes for over a week, except perhaps when decent folk are in bed! It is then that she prefers the warmth and comfort of the blue of day.

The Question

I must ask you the question –
I'd do it straight away,
But it's a trifle awkward,
Especially today:
Today I think is special,
A truly unique date,
So forgive my wish to clarify
Just how we'll celebrate.

Should it be with our old friends,
Who sing familiar songs,
In recognition of past time,
While yet these days are long?
Or should it be with whisky,
Matured in sherry casks,
And waiting for the moment
When someone's going to ask?

The thing is, I would hardly
Desire to chance my arm,
And risk I might offend you,
Or cause some other harm.

But I have to know the answer,
And to achieve this end,
I have to ask the question –
So sorry my old friend.

Perhaps direct enquiry though,
It now comes home to me,
May not in fact be needed –
No need to cause a scene.

Therefore I'll tiptoe gently,
On this delicate quicksand;
My question will appear in mist
To take you by the hand,
And lead you to the water's edge,
Where pale reflections lie;
The sweetness of the evening
Will greet you with a sigh.

I wonder whether you recall
Past evenings such as this –
Warm and heavy with such scents
As bless our scene with bliss.
And were you born on such an eve,
In fragile beauty's glow –
Kissed by angels of the light,
A hundred years ago?

The Changeling

One day in May I met a man –
He stopped me in the street;
He said: 'I'm sure we've met before,
Though true, 'twas short and sweet'.

"That's most unlikely", I replied,
"Your face seems quite unknown;
Your features strike me oddly
And your ears are overgrown".

"Your brows are stuck with bottled glue,
Your eyes are coals on stalks;
Your nose is blue, and twitches too –
Your beard is green, and forks".

'I meant to mention long ago',
He ventured with a sigh,
'That given psychic powers I have,
Exceed the human eye'.

'But you sped off in fear and dread,
To visit maiden aunts –
In Pimlico or some such place,
To take them to a dance'.

'Your story though bore far more holes
Than Emmental in June:
It was a pity, my dear sir,
I could not cast my rune'.

'But time it is for reckoning:
I must unveil my hand –
The one that's raised above my head,
Which bears a golden band'.

"Be off, you loon" escaped my lips,
"I've rarely heard such rot;
Please cast your rune into the ditch,
And leave me to my lot".

'No, no, dear sir, it cannot be,
I'm sent by those above,
To save you from a fate much worse
Than unrequited love'.

"That is very well and good",
I snorted, with a gap
Of time, enough for me to check
My reference on a map.

(My antennae had detected
A growing danger here –
So preparation for my flight
Seemed an excellent idea!)

"Well, unrequited love's not bad,
And I will chance my arm;
If not, I think that I may come
To unrequited harm!"

"Far from my fate you claim to save
Me from by magic powers,
The more I think I stand more chance
Of doom, as pass the hours".

'I feel I must remind you of
Our meeting in the past',
He carried on without demur,
His raised hand now half-mast.

'I think it was at Birling Gap,
Above the crumbling cliffs,
That first I spied you on the grass;
With lunch of cod and chips'.

'Your running shoes were on your feet,
With wings it seemed, attached;
I watched you streak above the grass,
With words – the merest snatch'.

'But then I knew you must be found,
Before such ill befell,
So search I did, from Lymm to Lydd,
Before I cast a spell'.

'I hardly care to use the tricks
That wizards demonstrate,
But in this case, my mirrored face
Told not to hesitate'.

'And now the powers have summoned you;
Our orbit we have found,
So I must validate my vow
To turn your case around'.

'Pray sit upon this tuft of grass,
While I prepare to act,
To save you from catastrophe –
A trip to hell and back.'

'Do contemplate: your mental state
Is crucial to success –
Consider hence the workings of
The monster of Loch Ness'.

'Its undulations sweet and soft,
That soothe the broken brain –
And mating call, so trenchant now,
With descant in refrain'.

'Its power and majesty to boot,
When cleaving through the loch,
With all its relatives in train –
The females in their frocks.'

"Oh, very well", I heard myself
Say to the sun in haze;
"I do confess my marbles aren't
As were in former days".

And sitting on the tuft I felt
A weariness come forth –
An inward ebb of strength it was,
Traversed from south to north.

And then I felt compelled to lie
Full length upon the grass,
As numbness overcame me,
And the sky turned overcast.

My saviour brought a candle lit
With bright flame from his coat,
And then a book with golden words,
And a bell in brass, and oats.

He next consumed the oats for strength,
But I sadly saw no more,
Though hear I could, as he declared
He was shaken to the core.

'I'm truly saddened my dear sir,
It seems a little late –
Despite my vast experience
Of arcane things to date'.

'I'm sure you've heard it said of those
Who are declining fast,
That they are fading quite away,
And can't expect to last'.

'At any rate, this sunken state
Is hardly risible:
With great regret, I must admit –
You're now invisible'.

How it pains me to relate,
That though I speak and hear,
I cannot see, nor can be seen.
Do I still live? I am not clear.

So if a man with bell of brass,
Gold book and candle too,
Should tell you you're in danger –
Let him attend to you!

*As you are no doubt aware, a 'changeling' is not the usual term to describe
a person as unfortunate as this one. However, I don't really know of
anything better – do you?*

Idle Fancy

When idle fancy takes me
By the hand, to bid me act,
I feel the call of wise old friends,
Who sign the way with freighted hands
A journey seeming well-defined
By footsteps of a previous mind –
Abandoned though long since.

But then the echoes of those prints
May live again in time to come;
At distant hours, when faded flowers
And misted days have gone:
Brought to mind and instant light
By old familiar haunts and scents,
And comforting coincidence.

Long Ago And Far Away

Long ago, and far away,
As all good stories used to say –
What was the matter of the day?
I can't recall – it's long ago,
And too far off to really know.

It's now today and right in front,
No need to wait or start a hunt,
With all dimensions here to stay –
So it seems and so you say;
But soon, in maybe just a day,
If marbles roll away and stray,
It's long ago, and far away.

Young Love

Tube trains compress you,
Buses break down;
Taxis will drop you –
Just out of town.

Horses need saddles,
Camels can snort;
Kayaks need paddles,
Ships don't leave port.

Rowing boats splash you,
Cars live in jams;
Motorbikes crash you –
And beware of the trams!

Skydiving's scary,
Submarines leak;
Lifts make you wary,
Trains come next week.

Cycles aren't comfy,
Planes are delayed;
And vans are so draughty –
You'll be so glad you stayed!

The Time Of Your Life

The past is gone now,
And as it's cast askance,
To be recorded
Forever and a day –
Infinity increases,
But memories may stay
To beat the fevered brow.

The present proves
That life at least exists,
Then – consumed by mist,
Cut down, and barely fit
To live an instant;
We can scarcely love it –
And the earth hardly moves.

The future beckons,
And that waving finger
Lures us ever closer to
The final dance,
That all forget,
But know just once:
The dead pool reckons.

*As it is the beginning of a new year, I thought we should
try to face it with spirited courage and cheerfulness.*

The Soul Of Gravity

Some years ago, when winter's
Icy cloak spread far from sight,
I came to earth; not fallen
Frozen from a leafless tree,
Nor risen rigid from the sea –
But hot in bed at still of night,
Now shattered by a primal scream.

But then the all-pervading
Fact came clear; I was betrayed.
No angels came in haste to save
Me from this puzzle known as life.
No warning sign – this seeming strife
Would haunt me, hunt me all my days,
Until cut free by unseen knife.

This life I spent in certain
Knowledge that the thing that kept
My head on earth, myself upright –
Prevented wanderings all about the sky,
No matter where, from whom or why,
The force that stopped my being swept
Away, was gravity – at least I tried.

Luckily the weight of work of
Mind was light, and disregarded
Newton's way, that sad blight
That keeps our cumbered lives in check,
With links and fetters, leg and neck –
But even so, earthbound with dread,
I plot and plan, yet stay on deck.

Ah, but what if nature's dice
Had fallen inward, upside down?
Given us entire the wings to fly,
In gossamer, not blood and bone;
Bodies not of sticks and stones –
The mind enhanced, its lightness found:
As one, the spirit and its home.

A Tense Affair

The present isn't perfect,
And it's over in a flash;
What used to be's imperfect
Too, and are we being rash
To hope the future's better?

There's no portent of it yet,
But with locked iron grip and fetter
Of the past and present set –
It permits the future perfect,
Though you're better off to bet
Against elusive theories:
Take the money – not regret!

This Life

This life's a stage, the curtain swept aside;
The actors in strange garb just pose and prance,
And joke and jest, and puff themselves with pride,
But hard it is to comprehend their dance.

There's music too; some tunes you may have heard,
Though not liked much, nor fitting to the plot –
Itself a weak and struggling half-winged bird,
And only fit for boiling in a pot.

There is no way to follow what goes on –
Aesthetically it scarcely meets a need;
All purpose, poise and structure simply gone –
A million voices waiting to be freed.

From time to time a fight breaks out on stage,
And someone in the wings gives noisy birth;
A drunken priest sways at his bible page –
Now put to high church music, causing mirth.

What is the point of such a tiresome dirge?
I wonder as the interval draws near;
My waiting whisky magnifies my urge
To flee, with burning coat tails at my rear.

I promise that I shall not darken doors
Through which I might again meet this offence;
Instead next time, when hailed through misty gauze,
I'll shout: 'No thanks – it simply makes no sense'.

The Law According To Murphy

Now everyone's heard about Murphy,
And he's only a heartbeat away,
Though it's really quite hard to detect him –
Until he goes wild one fine day.

Yes, Murphy is really a nuisance,
And sometimes he goes rather far;
Great it would be to ban Murphy,
To the darker side of some star!

But Murphy's had very good training –
He's a cousin of Satan's, it's said;
He loves to cause problems for people
Who worship their toast – or just bread!

You may like a trouble-free breakfast,
If last night you had a few beers;
Well, Murphy is watching and ready,
And you'll find he has other ideas!

So brandish your toast like a natural,
And cover with butter one side,
Add marmalade, all soft and squidgy,
As your jaws creak open so wide.

But this is just when dear Murphy
Then serves up his own evil dish –
When the marmalade's on and so sticky,
And your tongue's thinking 'oh how delish!'

You'll hear a loud noise, like a shotgun,
Or maybe a fast-slamming door –
In any case something that shocks you,
Into dropping your toast on the floor.

And that's not the end of it either,
As you utter a curse, with a frown;
The worst thing of all I must tell you:
The toast will land butter side down!

Well, that is old Murphy in action,
He aims to frustrate and reverse;
All of the good and the normal,
He just sees as bad and perverse!

So here's my advice in a nutshell:
When your toast is all ready to eat,
Use earplugs before you consume it,
And strap yourself into your seat!

I suppose it is just possible that you have never heard of Murphy's Law, which has other names sometimes. It is sometimes referred to jocularly as 'The Fourth Law of Thermodynamics'. In basic terms, it describes a very commonly experienced phenomenon – that if it is possible for something to go wrong, then it will!

Alternatively, even if we work really hard to prevent a disastrous outcome, we will almost always fail. It leads us to wonder about the desirability of any human activity, rather sadly! Fortunately, on about one occasion in every million, something actually goes the way it was meant to, greatly against our expectations. It is then that we often say that – yes, there is a God – assuming that we can remember the words!

Second Coming

The world's in waiting;
There's no more time.
It's all gone wrong –
There's too much crime.

The world's pulsating,
Yet it still spins;
How many are guilty –
How many sins?

The world's frustrating,
And it can't wait;
Too much corruption –
Never too late?

The world's all heating,
As climates change;
The sun seems so hot –
Is it so strange?

The world's still waiting,
But Jesus saves;
Can you see him –
Beyond huge waves?

About Us

Dick Dixon

Dick Dixon was born in Sawbridgeworth, Hertfordshire; he works as a teacher at a college on the south coast of England. While at Richard Hale school, as it is called now, he won the Ilott prize for poetry in 1962. He graduated in mathematics in 1970 from the University of Wales, as it was then, and embarked on a rather chequered career, involving an insurance company, a British Rail drawing office, and various other ventures.

Eventually, light appeared at the end of the tunnel, and he realised that the answer surely was to engage in the teaching of mathematics, (though the precise nature of the question has remained obscure).

Some time ago, in 2013, he met Reine Mazoyer, the French artist, and it became quite clear quite quickly that together, they would have to write their book 'Rhymes for no Reason' together, after which it seemed churlish not to continue with 'Rhymes of the Newfangled Màriner', 'The Curse of the Square Crow' and now the latest volume, 'In Bed with the Cats' Pyjamas'. We hope you will be able to detect something of interest in this this new book, or find a little something to remind you of a past time that is not far away, but just maybe seems that way. Perhaps one day, we can hope to get back to something nearer to the way we were, though it does seem that it will be a difficult task!

Reine Mazoyer

Reine Mazoyer is a French artist. She was born in Montbrison in southern France and graduated from the 'Ecole des Beaux-Arts' at Saint-Etienne in 1965.

She married Robert Mazoyer (who died in 1999), the well-known movie-film director, and worked with him as art director. Later she worked as a director for documentary movies. She exhibits her art creations regularly in Europe and the United States.

Reine received the honour of 'Chevalier des Arts et des Lettres' in 2008.

After having written and illustrated two books herself, Reine met Dick Dixon, and together they realised that they were definitely crazy enough to create more books! Reine has now illustrated four books in this series: 'Rhymes for no Reason', 'Rhymes of the Newfangled Mariner', ' The Curse of The Square Crow', and now the current volume 'In Bed with the Cats' Pyjamas'. There will most probably be more to come!

Dick Dixon and Reine Mazoyer at the Book Stop Café
in Eymet, France, in July 2016.

The author's niece Lucy with her birthday copy of
Rhymes of the Newfangled Mariner.

The original Square Crow, as constructed
by Reine Mazoyer.

Explications en Français pour 'In Bed with the Cats' Pyjamas'.

1/ Félicitations.

Les mariages sont une fête : un prêtre, des anneaux, des fleurs, des confettis, tout le monde prie et espère puis... tout est consommé au sommet de l' escalier branlant !

Baptiser un enfant, quelle joie : Champagne, Prosecco, tout pour humecter la tête du bébé. On dit Bravo à Fran et Fred pour leur participation à la chaine de l' humanité.

Les noces d'or sont émouvantes, incroyable comme le temps passe, cinquante ans déjà, de bétises et de joies, avec un gâteau et les baisers de vieux amis.

Un enterrement, c'est triste n'est ce pas, nos prières aident à dire « Adieu », une fusée de bois s'envole vers la porte du Paradis tandis que nous restons en larmes. Pas besoin de félicitations !

2/ Les Chats en Pyjamas.

Tout le monde sait que les chats aiment se reposer et dormir dans la journée , après leurs aventures de chasses nocturnes . Ces chats s'inquiètent de pas voir le soleil se lever le lendemain, alors, avant de partir chasser, ils se réunissent pour prier pour le retour du soleil le matin suivant. Ils offrent une sérénade au soleil, au cas où la prière ne serait pas suffisante. Ils ont remarqué que c'était efficace et recommencent chaque soir. Cependant, ils préfèrent être discrets, aussi portent- ils des pyjamas d'une couleur rose tendre plutôt que rouge vif.

3/ Mystères.

Il y a tellement de choses inexplicables... par exemple : pourquoi le soleil se lève à l'Est ? Comment font les hérissons pour faire l'amour sans se blesser ? Et pourquoi est- il si difficile d'enfourcher une bicyclette par le côté gauche ? La lune est-elle à l'envers en Australie et l'eau peut-elle être bénite directement en sortant du robinet si vous la faite bouillir ? En tant qu'être humain, je me demande si mon cœur est capable d' être fidèle, ses battements ont-ils le même son : « doki doki » à Tokyo ou « doogan doogan » en Corée ? Tout autour de moi des milliers de battements de coeur peuvent s'exprimer avec leurs propres langages, et sans aucun doute, mon coeur a son langage, donc son amour n'est pas constant et ne grandira pas tant qu'il existera.

4/ L'ile.

Le poète John Donne a écrit au 17 ème siècle ses 'Méditations' où l'on peu lire cette phrase célèbre : « Aucun homme n'est une ile ». Il avait sans doute écrit ce poème car il ne connaissait probablement pas l'ile de Man, qui se trouve dans la mer d'Irlande, entre la Grande Bretagne et l'Irlande. Le poème exprime la contradiction entre l'existence de l'ile de Man et ce que le poète John Donne avait écrit.

5/ La théorie de la Poudre (se tenir à carreau).

J'ai toujours conservé ma poudre au sec ... autrement dit , en Français, je me suis toujours « tenu à carreau », en cas de problème ! Mais cela ne m'a jamais aidé à résoudre quoi que ce soit. Il aurais mieux valu que « je me mouille » sans peur pour découvrir de nouveaux amis et tout ce que j'ai manqué en espérant l'inaccessible. Trop tard me direz vous, la pendule ne peut pas fonctionner à l'envers. Je resterai donc « sur le carreau ». Il vaut mieux « quitter la scène » et boire un bon coup !

6/ Mon Bouc.

Si vous marchez dans le parc, vous ne trouverez pas mon bouc ; vous ne voyez nulle part sa tête barbue couronnée de magnifiques cornes, typiques du Capricorne. Il est intelligent et cultivé, un petit peu snob, et il ne veut pas se mélanger aux autres. Il recherche le meilleur pour son palais raffiné : du caviar, un bon vin vieux - même si il a quelque difficulté à ouvrir la bouteille. Il se glisse dans la cuisine et ouvre la porte du frigo pour manger toutes les truffes que j'avais soigneusement cachées. Je dois me souvenir que c'est vraiment un sacré bouc !

7/ Restez à l'écart.

Eloignez-vous de l'explosion dans le ciel rougeoyant. Le monde réveille les esprits et les cœurs des morts. Le cri de la terre arrive trop tard ; l'obscurité va tout envahir ; la lune si proche, répand une vague après l'autre sur les prairies, les tombes, les rivières ; elle sauve ou inonde. Tandis que les forêts brûlent, les oiseaux s'envolent dans les rayons de lune. Il est trop tard, pas de reproches, pas de plaintes, c'est maintenant la fatalité, réveillez-vous avant de tomber en poussière. Fuyez!

8/ Un Saut dans l'inconnu.

Si vous souffrez de somnambulisme, prenez garde au trou qu'un jardinier a creusé dans le jardin ! Regardez-y à deux fois avant de faire un « saut dans l'inconnu »

Quoique ... il soit bon de se souvenir que « Le temps perdu ne se rattrape plus ! ».

9/ Les Genoux des Abeilles.

Sans aucun doute (du moins c'est ce que l'on dit) les abeilles ont de petits genoux.

Alors, une enquête est décidée pour confirmer cette affirmation : des journalistes et moi vont observer attentivement les mouvements des abeilles avec des lunettes d'approche.

A travers les buissons de roses, les fleurs parfumées, dans la prismatique lumière du soleil, nous découvrons une foule de petites abeilles agenouillées en adoration . Une abeille apparait, auréolée de lumière, accompagnée par les prières de la foule des implorantes : c'est Mélissa, la déesse des abeilles !

Comment vais -je pouvoir expliquer cette découverte à mon éditeur ? Evidemment, il ne me croie pas et préfère, dit- il, élever un troupeau de lamas, ou, ce qui lui semble plus intéressant, découvrir pourquoi les chats portent des pyjamas rose !

10/ Révélations de Dernière Minute.

Une dernière minute passe, cachée, silencieuse, tout près de la porte.

L'ami médecin a patiemment examiné et quand la consultation arrive à sa fin, nous savons qu'il faut dire la vérité. Pas besoin de pentothal ou d'huile de serpent ; le docteur attend calmement avec sympathie, bavarde un peu. Mais le temps passe, il faut se décider, avoir le courage de tout dire. Le docteur a un petit sourire. La main sur la poignée de porte, vous vous parlez enfin : Docteur, mon péché doit être confessé : je vois Sue - vous savez, votre délicieuse femme ... elle est un vrai trésor !

En Anglais on appelle cela « les révélations de la poignée de porte » , ce que l'on cache et ne dit qu' à la dernière minute.

11/ Le Festin de Minuit.

Quoi de plus approprié qu'un voyage au Tibet pour résoudre la plus part de vos problèmes ?

En tout cas, ma rencontre avec les extraordinaires moines qui y vivent m'a enseigné beaucoup plus que la méditation et la patience ! J'ai pu enfin expérimenter la lévitation en volant autour de ma chambre, pendant les chaudes nuits d'été, et me débarrasser, bouche grande ouverte, de tous ces moustiques agressifs qui ont finis leur courte existence dans mon estomac !

12/ Les Hommes que vous devez Rencontrer.

Les plombiers vont pleurer si vous leur dites que vous ne pouvez plus les voir, et les avocats vont vous demander d'être brève – sinon cela va vous couter cher ! Les docteurs vous remplissent de pilules avant d'inspecter vos maladies dans l'obscurité, et les professeurs vous diront que c'est l'heure de vous noter, à moins que vous ne pensiez à quelque chose de plus rapide. Les vendeurs vont chercher ce qu'ils ont de meilleur à vous proposer pour satisfaire vos envies, et les taxis doubleront le prix après minuit ; si vous ne caressez pas les vétérinaires, vous pourrez attraper la rage. Les électriciens vont mettre le contact et les voleurs vont fouiller vos tiroirs. Cela doit vous faire prendre conscience qu' il vaut mieux pour vous trouver un homme sans emploi !

13/ Les Raisons.

Il est arrivé quelque chose, mais je crains de ne pas pouvoir vous dire exactement quoi. Je peux vous expliquer les raisons qui ont causé ce qui est arrivé, même si je ne peux pas vous dire ce que c'est. Ce serait plus acceptable pour vous si je vous chantais ces raisons, après tout si c'est quelque chose de désagréable, cela serait plus supportable de le dire en musique ! Je pense que ces raisons sonneraient mieux en La Bémol mineur. J'ai une confession à vous faire : je ne peux pas chanter. En La Bémol mineur dites- vous ? j'ai déjà dit que je ne peux pas chanter ! Ne m'obligez pas à le répéter encore ! C'est un secret, jusqu' à ce que j'essaie de chanter !

Mais il y a une autre raison pour ne pas utiliser le La Bémol mineur., c'est la langue ! Le langage de l'écriture musicale est différent en Anglais du langage utilisé en Français. Un La Bémol mineur se traduit par : un A (La) flat (Bémol mais aussi Plat) minor(Mineur)... vous allez donc comprendre pourquoi un piano tombant sur un groupe de mineurs.... Va donner : « A flat minor » ... AH AH !

14/ Le Temps.

Le Temps est étrange. Il arrive toujours tard, alors tout vieillit. Il y a là un étrange manque de symétrie, alors que d' autres choses peuvent être changées.

Vous devez attendre pour découvrir ce qui va arriver et même si nous faisons un plan très précis, nous ne sommes jamais certains que quelque chose d'imprévu ne va pas arriver.

De toute façon, ceux qui veulent changer les règles et trouver ce que le futur nous réserve découvrirons bientôt qu'ils en sont empêchés par le « Gardien du Futur ». Si ce n'était pas vrai, je miserai gros sur un cheval dans la prochaine course.

15/ Pluie d'Or.

En Angleterre, nous parlons toujours de la pluie. Mais plutôt que d'en parler, nous devrions la recueillir, sinon cette merveilleuse substance est perdue !

Nous proposons de fabriquer une sorte de chapeau, un chapeau qui puisse recueillir la pluie afin de l'utiliser plus tard, peut-être pour faire du thé. Les avantages sont multiples, particulièrement celui de ne pas avoir besoin de parapluie !

16/ Un Etat de Sainteté?

Il y avait un homme qui vivait au dernier étage des appartements de mon immeuble. Il faisait toujours beaucoup de bruit en montant. Il semblait avoir un problème insoluble.

Un jour, il décida gréer une Montgolfière et de partir voyager dans le ciel, sans que nous, dans nos appartements, comprenions pourquoi. Il resta longtemps dans sa Montgolfière, au dessus de nous, et nous étions inquiets . Nous décidâmes de le faire redescendre, pour sa sécurité et nous le fîmes ! Mais quelle ne fut pas notre surprise de découvrir qu'il n' y avait plus personne dans la nacelle quand la Montgolfière redescendit !

A ce moment, une voix tonitruante résonna dans le ciel : « La réponse est oui ! D'accord, j'étais l' homme du dernier étage !

J'ai pensé « Ah ... je vois » Nous avons tous été très honoré de l' avoir eu vivant parmi nous.

17/ Le Cœur des Betteraves.

L'amour est juste une grosse betterave, bien rouge. Elle attend, solitaire, une petite larme de vinaigre au coin de l'œil , que la reine des fées des betteraves lui fasse rencontrer la betterave de ses rêves. Peut-être qu'un chef inspiré va enfin organiser leur rencontre, en compagnie d' un poisson, au centre d' une belle tarte, juste un homme et une femme avec un peu de sauce tartare - et, à minuit sonnante, sous le regard de la lune et des étoiles, sur la même assiette, ils vont pouvoir être réunis !

18/ Drôles de Temps

Mon Dieu, le mercure va-t-il cesser de monter ? La pluie va -t-elle devenir autre chose qu un torrent qui inonde le centre des villes, transformant les voitures en bateaux ?

En même temps, ailleurs, va-t-il enfin pleuvoir pour que les cultures redeviennent normales ?

Que va-t-il arriver au niveau de la montée des eaux ? Nos villes côtières vont-elles cesser   d' être menacées ? Le Monde va-t-il devenir un vaste océan avec quelques iles émergeantes ?

Nous pourrions mieux contrôler le climat si nous tentions ensemble de faire ce qui devrait être fait. Il y a beaucoup à faire, mais nous pouvons petit à petit modifier notre style de vie et commencer aujourd'hui ! Nous devons penser à ceux qui vont habiter ce monde dans le futur n'est-ce-pas ?

19/ Sain et sauf chez soi.

Dehors, les arbres sont tordus par le vent, un chien aboie, répondant au hululement de la chouette accompagnée par des hurlements de loups. Maintenant la terre entre dans l'obscurité, les gargouilles ricanent, les esprits malfaisants se déchainent, et nous, humains, devons espérer une renaissance. Allons-nous être enveloppés par les terreurs de la nuit ? Restons calmes ! J' ai imaginés ces visions terrifiantes à travers une vitre embuée et j'ai beaucoup de chance d'être chez moi, loin des démons et des terreurs de la nuit. La pendule accompagne mes battements de cœur, un chien fidèle se frotte à mes jambes. Un bon feu réchauffe la pièce pleine de roses et un « Nuits Saint Georges » adoucit mon sommeil. Un Canaletto, de l'argenterie, une maison remplie de musique, amour et lumière ! C'est là que je veux être cette nuit, s'il vous plait mon Dieu !

20/ Le Vicaire de Stiffkey

Le poème nous conte la triste histoire de Harold Davidson
qui, après avoir eu divers emplois pour l' église à Londres,
était devenu le Vicaire de Stiffkey, dans le Nord du Norfolk en
Angleterre, en 1906. Il avait travaillé auparavant à aider des
femmes prostituées à Londres et s'était totalement engagé
dans ce sacerdoce, même dans le Norfolk ! Il continuait d'
aller à Londres pour être certain que cette partie de son travail
était toujours utile. Mais, l' Evêque de Norwich (Norfolk) ayant
entendu parler de cet engagement a manifesté sa désapprobation,
ce qui a conduit notre pauvre Vicaire à être défroqué et à
chercher un autre emploi. Il avait été acteur dans le passé et a pu
entrer dans un cirque montrant des lions !

Malheureusement, en Juillet 1937, alors qu'il domptait des lions
en cage pour le public, il a marché sur la queue d'un des lions
qui s'est retourné contre lui et l'a attaqué. Il est mort à l' hôpital
quelques jours plus tard.

21/ Nettoyage par aspirateur (ou nettoyage par le vide).

Le nettoyage par aspirateur existe depuis longtemps maintenant. Les tapis de la nation doivent être fiers de tous les efforts effectués pour les garder propres !

L' incroyable mais passionnante nouvelle est que cela n'était pas nécessaire ! Pourquoi allez vous me demander ? Bien, c'est simplement qu'un aspirateur ne contient rien... mais pour cela, vous devez connaître la traduction du mot Anglais Vacuum qui signifie « Vide »... alors ce sera plus facile ! Evidemment vous comprenez maintenant que votre «Vacuum » ne contient rien, ni poussière, ni miettes de vos gâteaux et biscuits, non, c' est un territoire vierge, alors, comment peut- il être nettoyé ?

Exactement ! Alors rangez votre aspirateur (ou hoover en Anglais, encore une autre traduction !) partez et faite l' amour sur la pelouse pour célébrer cette découverte !

22/ Ode à Séléné.

Je vous regarde contempler la pleine lune, silencieuse et argentée, suspendue dans la nuit.

Deux semaines vont passer, mesurant son déclin, puis son lent retour. Qu'a- t-elle à nous dire ? Pouvons- nous entendre ses lointaines complaintes ? Puis elle dissimule son visage dans le bleu saphir du jour. Peut-être allons-nous consulter l'oracle , faire une prière pour comprendre sa souffrance ?Depuis des millions d'années nous existons et grandissons dans la grotte de Platon, sans rien comprendre. C'est facile pour vous et moi de nous cacher ce qui se trouve en pleine lumière, au fur et à mesure que le jour passe, les mots trouvent le « pourquoi ». Un jour proche, nous comprendrons que notre amour restera enfermé tant que nous n'en aurons pas la clé.

23/ Une Histoire de Temps

Le présent va trop vite ; il est imparfait, mais pouvons - nous espérer un meilleur futur ?

Rien n'est certain, mais avec des chaines et cadenas autour du passé et du présent, le futur peux devenir parfait, quoiqu'il soit plus prudent de ne pas parier sur ces théories fumeuses, conserver votre argent – c'est plus sûr !

24/ La Rencontre.

Un homme atteint d'une maladie inconnue rencontre son ange gardien. Mais cet ange gardien est tellement effrayant que notre homme s'enfuit en courant !

Plus tard, ils se retrouvent et l'ange essaie encore de soigner son protégé avec des formules magiques, hélas il est trop tard ... l' homme devient invisible.

La morale de cette histoire est : prenez rendez-vous avec votre médecin avant qu'il ne soit trop tard !

25/ Pensées Fugitives.

Quand une pensée fugitive me prend par la main, je sens l' appel
d'ancien amis. Ils me montrent le chemin, agitant leurs mains,
m' invitant à un voyage dans le passé, puis s'effacent dans le
brouillard. Les échos de leur présence vivent encore un peu,
comme les fleurs fanées gardent encore un peu de leur odeur et
de leurs couleurs, souvenirs réconfortants.

26/ Très Loin, il y a Longtemps.

Quand quelque chose s'est produit il y a longtemps et très loin de là où vous êtes maintenant, il semble normal que vous ne vous souveniez que de peu de choses à ce sujet mais que se passe-t-il si c'est arrivé juste en face de vous, aujourd'hui ? C'est difficile de penser que vous ne vous en souviendrez pas demain, à moins que vous ne soyez en meilleure forme auparavant. Il semble que nous acceptions cette sorte de détérioration au fur et à mesure que le temps passe. Oh là là !

27/ Jeune Amour

Il faut faire attention avant d'utiliser les moyens de transport. N' importe lesquels.

Métros, taxis, autobus, trains, trams, sous-marins, etc, vous allez vous en rendre compte.

Ils vont mal fonctionner un jour ou l'autre et vous laisser tomber. Vous pourriez vous retrouver bloquée dans un endroit horrible et froid. C'est beaucoup mieux de rester dans mon chaud et confortable appartement ; je promets que vous ne le regretterez pas !

28/ Le Temps de Vivre.

Ce poème nous alerte tous. Il montre ce qui peut arriver si vous ne regardez pas du bon côté des choses. Si vous analysez en détail le passé, le présent ou le futur, vous pouvez les rendre terrifiants. Il n'y a pas moyen d'y échapper puisque nous sommes prisonniers du Temps.

Je suis maintenant moi-même terrifié et je vais tenter de résoudre ce problème autant que possible, pour célébrer cette évidence que je suis vivant, ici et maintenant, à cette minute, et que nous avons laissé le moyen âge très loin dans le passé, grâce à Dieu !

29/ La Gravité de l'Ame.

Je veux juste vous faire part de mes découvertes au sujet de la vie, de l'univers et... un peu de tout finalement.

Honnêtement, la vie, c'est compliqué. Aussitôt que j'ai eu conscience de mon existence, je me suis demandé ce que je pourrai bien en faire. Il y a tellement à faire, c'est vrai, mais quelle était ma tâche ? La seule chose dont j'étais certain était la gravité. C'était la seule chose qui me permettait, à moi et à mon corps de rester sur terre. Si j'avais eu le choix, je pense que je serais parti explorer le ciel, quel bonheur !

Quel dommage que l'existence n'ai pas été différente- ces deux aspects : corps et âme auraient pu ne pas subir ensemble la malédiction de la gravité, alors nous aurions pu être capable d' être des esprits pendant notre vie.

Je pense que certains ne seront pas d'accord, mais, hein, personne n'est parfait !

30/ La Question.

Certaines questions sont difficiles à poser. Demanderiez-
vous à une dame si elle a prévu d' empoisonner son mari ?
Demanderiez- vous à un monsieur pourquoi sa braguette n'est
pas bien fermée ?

Vous risquez de ne pas recevoir la réponse que vous attendiez.

La question qui nous intéresse n'est pas trop difficile, mais peut-
être un peu embarrassante.

Il s'agit de demander à votre vieille amie si elle va avoir 100 ans,
à moins que ce ne soit 99 !Dans ce cas, la réponse risque d'être
surprenante !

31/ Cette vie.

Souvent, la vie est pleine de surprises, d'espoir, de couleurs. C'est tout ce que nous avons et c'est très précieux pour nous car, sans cela, que serions nous ?

Et pourtant, n'est-il pas surprenant que nous existions après tout ? Quand nous observons les êtres humains faire toutes les choses étranges qu'ils font souvent, nous demandons nous « pourquoi » ? Sont-ils si différents de nous ? Combien de personnes y a -t-il dans ce « nous » ? Une seule peut-être ? Pouvons-nous comprendre le sens de la vie et être prêt à une seconde chance? Nous devons réfléchir à cette question et nous préparer à y répondre si nécessaire !

32/ La Loi de Murphy.

Tout le monde connaît Murphy. C'est un sale type ; on voudrait pouvoir l'expédier du côté obscur des étoiles, mais il est toujours là ; c'est un cousin de Satan. Murphy adore causer des problèmes à ceux qui prennent leur petit déjeuner. Vous aimez beurrer votre toast et même y ajouter de la confiture, mais au moment où vous portez la tartine à votre bouche , une porte claque et c'est là que Murphy entre en action ! Il fait toujours tomber votre toast sur la moquette, du côté du beurre et de la confiture ! Alors, suivez mon conseil : avant de prendre votre petit déjeuner, mettez des boules Quies et attachez- vous fermement à votre fauteuil !

33/ Deuxième Apparition.

Le monde est en attente ; c'est urgent - tout va mal et trop de crimes. Le monde palpite, mais combien de fautifs ? Combien de péchés ? Le monde est frustré et il ne peut plus attendre - trop de corruption, mais jamais trop tard ?Le monde se réchauffe , mais le soleil brûle - n'est- ce pas étrange ? Le monde attend toujours mais Jésus sauve ! Ne le voyez -vous pas derrière les énormes vagues ?

BV - #0047 - 240522 - C112 - 229/152/11 - PB - 9781861518088 - Gloss Lamination

WHISTLE FOR THE CI

Cathleen paused to look out of the long
windows over the darkening countryside.
There was a misshapen tree just beyond the
garden. One side must have been cut off by
lightning, and now it thrust out one leafless
crooked bough which was loaded to breaking-
point with crows. They were fighting and
croaking and flying in black circles as one by
one they were dislodged by their jostling
fellows.
Crows, not cats. Birds not babies.
She dreamed she heard the baby crying again
that night. But when she woke up she was
crying herself.

And it was dawn, and the crows, gathered on
the crooked tree, were beginning to croak and
squabble.
The tree was a scarecrow like herself,
inhabited only with the black birds of
sorrow ...

Whistle
For the Crows

Dorothy Eden

CORONET BOOKS
Hodder and Stoughton

Copyright © 1962 Dorothy Eden

First published in Great Britain 1962 by
Hodder and Stoughton Limited

Coronet Edition 1965
Second Impression 1968
Third Impression 1969
Fourth Impression 1972
Fifth Impression 1973
Sixth Impression 1976
Seventh Impression 1976

Printed and bound in Great Britain for
Coronet Books, Hodder and Stoughton, London,
By Cox & Wyman Ltd, London, Reading and Fakenham

ISBN 0 340 01923 9

CHAPTER ONE

THE baby began to cry in the night.

Cathleen was awake instantly. Tense and miserable, she lay listening. At least this time it was not Debby come back to haunt her in a dream, for the sound went on, a desolate wailing that suggested some poor little creature abandoned forever. She knew that she wouldn't sleep again until the sound stopped.

It must be near morning, for faint grey light came in the window. It was the grey of the Dublin streets and the low sky, and the slaty rooftops. Everything had seemed grey since she had arrived last evening. She had felt homesick (for where?), and even more alone than usual. Her sense of adventure, which Ronald Gault had been so sure this trip would arouse, seemed to have left her altogether. At this lowest peak of the day she didn't know how she was going to face Miss Matilda O'Riordan later in the morning, and show interest in the position offered.

It took only the forlorn sound of the baby crying to complete her loss of morale.

All at once, everything was quiet. It had been a momentary nightmare. Ireland was not always a land of tears, as it had seemed last evening, tears of rain, of farewells on docksides and airports, of old shawled women waving tremulously to departing children and grandchildren, of orphaned babies . . .

It was also a land of kindness and zany jokes and gaiety. It was where she was to begin her life again.

And in full daylight she caught the zany gaiety, for when she pulled her curtains aside she found her window faced on to a low roof, on which sat five lean and hungry

5

cats. There were her crying babies, five of them, no less. Their green eyes looked up at her expectantly, and she thought that she probably resembled them herself, with her too thin triangular face, her smooth, fair hair, and her green eyes eagerly asking, not for the food the cats wanted to fill their stomachs, but for something to fill her heart.

That was what was wrong with her, an empty heart.

She rang for breakfast, and when it came, tossed scraps of bacon to her tabby and ginger friends.

'Good luck,' she called to them. 'And you might wish me the same.'

She would need it, for Ronald had warned her that old Miss O'Riordan was something of a dragon who would certainly lash secretaries and other employees with a fiery breath.

'She scared the wits out of me on the telephone,' Ronald said, 'You'll have to have stamina and a thick skin. But it will do you good. After all, there's a castle, too.'

Ronald, a publisher of repute, for whom she read and did revising and rewriting jobs, had sensibly decided that six months was long enough to grieve for a husband and child. Cathleen knew he was right. Jonathon and her baby, sweet eighteen-months-old Debby, killed in that tragic accident, had gone out of her life, and she now had to rebuild it. Friends who sympathized too much, and familiar surroundings, only served to keep her grief alive. She needed the bracing tonic of a new country and a challenging and interesting job. Even a dragonish old woman and a castle!

Miss O'Riordan was staying at the Gresham, and had arranged the appointment for eleven o'clock.

In her eagerness, Cathleen arrived too early. She went into the bar to smoke a cigarette and have an innocuous glass of tomato juice. She had a cautious feeling that Miss O'Riordan, although breathing flames herself, was quite

6

likely to notice even a hint of sherry on someone else's breath.

There was a scattering of people in the bar. Cathleen sat at a table in a corner. At the next table a man with wild dark hair and a gipsy brown face seemed to be struggling to write a letter. He was drinking whisky, and called for another one as Cathleen sat down. When the waiter brought it he drank it in a single swallow, stared for a few moments broodingly into space, then, with sudden impatience, tore up the paper he was writing on, put the scraps in his pocket, and went out. He was a little unsteady on his feet.

He must be having an unhappy love affair, Cathleen thought. He was trying unsuccessfully to put his passionate plea to his girl into writing. She noticed that one strip of the torn letter had fallen to the floor. Full of curiosity as to how the Irish expressed themselves under those circumstances, she picked it up and read the sprawling writing.

Moira should have come to her senses before it was too late. The next sentence was obscured, but after that was the shocking cryptic statement ... *deserves to be murdered, but you can't kill the golden goose.*

It was far from being a love letter. It also was not ill-spelt, and the man, for all his wild appearance, expressed himself like someone who had had education.

Moira ... It was a pretty name. It was better used in terms of love than in terms of money.

Cathleen dropped the paper distastefully. She had always heard of the love of the Irish for drama and wild exaggerations. Here was such an example. Nevertheless, she felt as if she had touched something poisonous. That man ought to be more careful. If he was going to make threats, he shouldn't get drunk, and leave evidence lying about.

But it was no business of hers, and it was time to have

7

herself announced to Miss Matilda O'Riordan. She smiled wryly, thinking that what with cats sounding like abandoned babies on doorsteps, and drunk Irishmen dropping half-written threats, she was getting into the swing of life over here. Now she could take Miss O'Riordan in her stride.

Cathleen had second thoughts about this when she came face to face with the old lady.

Miss O'Riordan was still in bed. She sat propped up with pillows, and wrapped in a sable cape. Her white hair was meant to be knotted on the top of her head, but various strands had escaped and were hanging with an air of wild abandon round her face. Her eyes were slitted and terribly observant, her nose remarkably long and thin. Her skin was exquisite. So were her fine narrow hands, folded with exactitude outside the sheets. She made an unforgettable picture. Like some old conspiring queen, Cathleen thought, the kind who would slip poison into a glove, or watch an execution with the air of a connoisseur.

'Come closer,' she ordered.

Cathleen obeyed, murmuring, 'Good morning, Miss O'Riordan.'

'Stand nearer the window where the light's better.'

Cathleen stood stockstill.

'I thought it was a secretary you wanted, Miss O'Riordan!'

'Did I say it wasn't? Did I also add a certain pleasing appearance is necessary? After all, I have to look at you when we're working, don't I? I have very fine sensibilities. That's better. Now I can see you.'

She stared for an embarrassingly long time.

'H'm,' she said at last. 'You don't overdress, I'm glad to see.' She tucked the sables closer round her long scrawny throat, adding, 'And if you're looking at me, don't. This fur is almost as old as I am myself. My mother gave it to me for my eighteenth birthday. Thought it would get me a husband perhaps. It didn't. Never depend entirely on clothes. It's personality that counts. Mine was too overpowering. I have no regrets.'

She folded her hands again and stared.

'I believe you're a widow.'

'Yes, Miss O'Riordan.'

'Not the flighty kind?'

'Really—'

'Very well, I suppose you were in love with your husband?'

Jonathon. The face that now belonged to a dream. Yes, she had been in love with him, but had he ever loved her, truly and completely? She had never known. Men were different from women. They hated to give themselves away, perhaps to put themselves too completely in a woman's power. Jonathon had made love, then drawn back into himself. She had never quite reached him. Had he been self-sufficient, or not really in love? Now she would never know, and at first the thought had tormented her unendurably. She had been a wife and a mother, and yet uncertain of being loved.

Would this old woman lying in the bed understand that?

'Yes, I loved my husband.'

'You don't still brood, I hope. I can't stand melancholy.'

'No. I don't brood.'

'Good. You seem to have acquired self-discipline. I hope you're good-tempered. This London publisher suggests that you can spell and put sentences together constructively. I propose writing a family history, as Mr. Gault has probably told you. He doesn't know that the manuscript will probably burn his fingers.' She gave a snort of laughter. 'Drat! Who's that? Come in!'

The sharp knock at the door was followed by the entrance of a tall, dark-haired young man.

9

'Good lord, Aunt Tilly, you aren't even up!'

'And why should I be?'

'I want to get started.'

'Started for home! My dear boy, you'll have to change your plans. I have not only a day's shopping, but I must visit the orphanage. I promised Sister Mary Martha. One has to have some thought for others. I give myself all the time. From the minute I woke this morning I've met nothing but demands, demands, demands.' For a moment her face was old, narrow-eyed, crafty. She looked at the young man beneath her eyelids. She seemed to be searching his face for something. In a minute she had relaxed and added shortly, 'You'll simply have to wait for me.'

'I'll do nothing of the kind. If you're not ready to leave this morning I'll go by train. You can follow in the car. Kitty can drive.'

'Kitty! And land us all in the ditch. Mrs. Lamb, can you drive an ancient Rolls?'

Never having driven one in her life, Cathleen answered calmly that she could. She was aware of the young man's eyes on her. If he had noticed her presence earlier he had given no sign. Now he looked at her for a moment, then turned on his heel.

'See you at Loughneath, Aunt Tilly.'

The door banged. He was gone.

Miss O'Riordan threw off the sable wrap, disclosing a pair of sallow-skinned bony shoulders.

'That was my nephew Rory. A bad-mannered young man, as you could see. He'll have his own way, come plagues or persecutions. Kitty!'

The last word was said in a high demanding voice. Immediately the connecting door opened and a girl hurried in, limping. She had very wide blue eyes. She looked startled and helpless. The rude young man had been very much the kind of person one would associate with Miss O'Riordan's family, but this timid creature could surely only be a lady's maid in a state of perpetual nervousness.

'Yes, Aunt Tilly? You wanted me?'

'This is Mrs. Lamb, my secretary. This is my niece, Kitty, Mrs. Lamb. Rory's sister. I have one other nephew, Liam, whom you'll find a good deal more agreeable than his brother. Kitty, give me my wrap and my slippers and run my bath. We've got to get moving. The visit to the orphanage will take at least an hour. I want to arrange for some of the children to have a day at the castle, and that will take endless discussion. You know what Sister Mary Martha is.'

'Yes, Aunt Tilly.'

The little figure with the limp – one leg seemed to be shorter than the other – hurried to the bathroom. Cathleen looked away in some embarrassment as two thin shanks emerged from the bedclothes.

'Is there anything you want me to do at present, Miss O'Riordan?'

'Where are your things?'

'At my hotel.'

'Then go and fetch them. Don't hurry. If it's your first visit to Dublin you might like to take a look round. Be back here by four o'clock. We'll want to be home in time for dinner. Is that clear?'

'Yes, Miss O'Riordan. And thank you—'

'For what?'

'For giving me this opportunity.'

'Wait and see if you can make a success of it before you thank me. I expect genuine literary ability. And I'm a tyrant. Kitty will tell you. Kitty!'

The little figure in the plain dress re-emerged from the bathroom.

'Yes, Aunt Tilly.'

'Aren't I a tyrant?'

'Oh, no, Aunt Tilly. Why, where would we have been—'

II

'Well, never mind, never mind. Gratitude is a bore.'

Miss O'Riordan flapped a hand, and Kitty turned away. But not before Cathleen had caught a flicker of something behind the girl's wide-eyed perpetual startlement. What was it? Hate? Or fear?

The sun shone intermittently. Great clouds passed over the city, so that one moment the streets and rooftops sparkled and the next were in gloom. The city reflected Cathleen's own mood as she walked down the long straight streets with their pleasingly symmetrical rows of smoky brick houses. The beautiful Georgian doorways and the long windows seemed too austere and discreet for the turbulent life they no doubt enclosed. From her first encounter with the Irish, Cathleen didn't think that dullness would be one of their characteristics. Even poor little Kitty with her subdued face and lame leg may have a tiny cauldron of something bubbling inside her. And if she had, Cathleen was pretty certain that Aunt Tilly's complacent assumption that it was gratitude was wrong.

Another thing – she imagined Aunt Tilly was at daggers drawn with her nephew Rory with his high-held head. They would be too much alike. They probably waged a continual battle for supremacy. It promised to make life lively, at the least. With relief, Cathleen knew that now she was glad about the job. Already she felt as if she had been injected with new blood. The ghost of little Debby, and the curiously guilty one of Jonathon, were drawing away.

She walked by the Liffey, its water as grey as the walls enclosing it. Someone somewhere was singing . . .

> And if not mine, dear girl,
> My snowy-breasted pearl . . .
> I'll never from the fair with life return . . .

The Irish were always talking or singing about fairs.

They had become a sort of symbol to them, Cathleen supposed, another word for happiness, or living. It was probably all the gaiety most of them had ever had. Their songs were full of tenderness and that threat of death – death from war or treachery or love or lack of love. Death full of drama and tragedy . . .

The sun went in again, and Cathleen couldn't repress a faint shiver. She listened for the man to sing something with less of that beautiful melancholy. Suddenly she saw him, a beggar on the humped bridge over the river. He had an accordion, and as she approached he began to play creakingly an Irish jig. He wasn't the singer, after all, but he had a merry wrinkled face, the colour of the purple foxgloves in the hedges.

She put sixpence in the dirty tweed cap lying at his feet, and he gave her a toothless smile. 'God bless yer pretty face, dear.' And the sun came out again.

The compliment had been the automatic response to her sixpence, but abruptly the thought went through her head that other people might find her pretty, too. Rory O'Riordan, and his brother, Liam? Foolish, she told herself. That new injection of blood mustn't prove troublesome.

Nevertheless, she was on a see-saw, or this country was. For ten minutes later, in her stroll along the river side, she came on an old woman, a black shawl over her head, her straggling hair the colour of dirty snow. The old woman took her arm, pointed at the river, and said inexplicably, 'Red hair turns black in water. Did ye know that?'

'No, I didn't.' Cathleen didn't like the dirty bony claw on her arm.

'It does, then. I saw it.'

Now the day dragged badly, and Cathleen was glad when it was time to go back to the hotel and see if the ladies were ready to leave.

Kitty answered her knock, and motioned to her to come into the room adjoining her aunt's.

'Some unexpected business has come up for my aunt. She doesn't want to be disturbed for a little while. I can't even finish her packing. Will you sit down, Mrs. Lamb.'

Kitty was quite polite, and spoke in a breathless voice as if she were shy. But she wasn't friendly.

Cathleen tried to establish some contact with the strange little creature.

'Did you have a successful morning?'

'We went shopping. Aunt Tilly bought a new hat and a dinner dress. Black velvet. It makes her look wonderful. She loves clothes. She keeps all her old ones. There's a room full of them at Loughneath.'

'And what about you?' Cathleen asked.

'Me? Oh, I don't care about clothes. I haven't the right sort of figure.'

She was painfully thin and small, but if it weren't for her limp, which seemed to come from some hip injury, she would have been reasonably easy to dress. Her soft fine hair was pretty. It was a pity she took refuge in a rather aggressive unattractiveness.

Guessing the subject of Kitty was a prickly one, Cathleen changed it.

'Your aunt must be a very generous person.'

'Why?'

'I thought she said something about an orphanage—'

'Oh, yes. St. Mary and Joseph's. It's her pet charity. She likes to go and see the children, but they – ' Kitty gave a tiny snicker, ' – are scared stiff of her. I used to be, too, when I was little.'

And she still was, Cathleen thought. She wondered what Liam was like as a brother, for Rory obviously would have little sympathy for someone so jumpy and nervous as his sister. If Liam were also arrogant and impatient and selfish, poor Kitty must have a lonely life.

'The children are to come to the castle for a day in June,' Kitty went on. 'About twenty of them do this every year. It's a frantic day, I'm warning you. Usually someone gets sick or scared or lost, or breaks a window, or runs over Patsy's flowerbed, and either Patsy or Mary Kate gives notice. The sisters at the orphanage think it's a doubtful blessing, but they can't tell Aunt Tilly that. She thinks she's being God for the day.'

Cathleen laughed, then wished she hadn't, because Kitty was completely serious. She was stating a simple fact.

And it wasn't hard to imagine Miss Matilda O'Riordan in the position of a deity, for at that moment her voice sounded from the next room. She must have been speaking all the time in a lower tone, but now something had made her angry, and she said penetratingly:

'Don't you dare to talk to me like that! You'll agree to my terms or there'll be nothing at all. And when it comes to a matter of conscience, it's yours you should be concerned about, not mine.'

The telephone slammed down. Kitty, Cathleen noticed, was standing perfectly still listening, her eyes enormous with some kind of apprehension. But as soon as footsteps sounded next door she returned to her work, and was innocently folding skirts and underclothing when Miss O'Riordan flung open the door.

'We're late and we're leaving immediately,' she said. 'Good heavens, Kitty, haven't you finished that packing yet. Come along, girl, come along. Where's my coat and hat? Ring for someone to take down the luggage, Mrs. Lamb. One would think, with the two of you – as if I haven't had enough trouble already with that scrounging scoundrel. Is everyone in this world crazy?'

Kitty looked up.

15

'Who have you had trouble with, Aunt Tilly?'

'Oh – that man I employed to do repairs at the orphanage. He'd take the food out of the children's mouths. Now get this packing finished and the bags sent down, and the car brought to the door.'

She swept back into the other room, slamming the door. Kitty worked in silence, shutting the bags and fastening them. Cathleen rang for the hotel porter, and by the time Miss O'Riordan re-emerged everything had been sent down.

She thought this might make the old lady relax, but the thin lips remained as tightly pressed, the narrowed eyes shot sparks.

'Are we ready? Then let's go. I've been upset, so I warn you I'm not in a good mood. *My* conscience indeed! The impertinence of him! Who has committed the crime? No one but – Kitty, what are you goggling at? Mrs. Lamb, go on ahead and see that the car's at the door.'

The car, with its highly-polished old-fashioned body, was waiting.

Cathleen climbed into the driving seat and began to study the controls. It was a moment before she noticed the dark face looking in the other window.

The man tapped and she leaned over to open the door. 'What do you want?'

'Would you ever buy one of my pots, lady? Or a fine kettle? I've seven children at home, praise God!'

The hotel porter had seen the man and was advancing menacingly.

'Get out of here, you rascal! Go on! Make yourself scarce!'

The man gathered his pots and pans together with a clatter.

'God give you a safe journey, lady . . .' He grinned irrepressibly, his dark eyes gleaming. He looked back once as he went.

Cathleen stared after him thoughtfully. Where had she seen that black-brown face before?

'I'm sorry, miss,' the porter was saying. 'Begging right on the doorstep. They're getting so cheeky, there's nothing to be done with them. I'd string them up, the divils!'

It couldn't have been the man writing the letter in the bar, and then crumpling it up . . . For that had been this morning, and he had been drunk. He would be at home now, sleeping off his threats of murder and revenge. If he had a home, and didn't live in a tinker's cart pulled by a donkey. For the face had been remarkably similar . . . Not so sinisterly dark, not so deliberately ragged and untidy. But if he had dressed to look like a tinker he would have looked exactly like that . . .

God give you a safe journey . . .

The words were glib, and spoken without thought. But suddenly Cathleen felt that they were needed. She was growing as morbidly superstitious as the local inhabitants . . .

CHAPTER TWO

THE road twisted between high green hedges, it ran through small austere grey villages and past empty fields. It was a peaceful road, inhabited chiefly by small children walking home from school hand in hand, sauntering priests, farm lads on bicycles, carts drawn by pattering donkeys and an occasional flock of geese.

To Cathleen it was an entirely pleasant journey into the last century. The country beneath the rolling storm clouds was exquisitely green and peaceful.

Half-way to Loughneath, Miss O'Riordan recovered her animation. It was as if she had been silently reflecting on a problem, and had at last resolved it. For her brow cleared and she said in her resonant voice,

'I have it! We'll make a change this year. We'll have the little ones.'

'The what, Aunt Tilly?'

'The younger children, stupid. We've always had the older ones, which is hardly fair. Let's have the little ones this year. I'll telephone Sister Mary Martha when we get home.'

'But, Aunt Tilly, wouldn't they – I mean, it's a long journey for little ones.'

'Nonsense! They're tough. They have to be, poor divils. Well, that's settled. Mary Kate will love it.'

'Love it!'

'Of course she will. You know how she and Patsy always wanted a baby. So the little ones will upset her much less than the big ones. There won't be all that unpleasantness about hurley games on the front lawn. She'll forgive misdemeanours, and so will Patsy. What do you think, Mrs. Lamb?'

'Well, I—'

'Come, you must know whether you like small children or not? Did you never want a baby of your own?'

Cathleen's hands tightened on the steering wheel.

'I had one,' she said.

'Then where is it, good God? You haven't had it adopted, you heartless creature!'

The story would have to be told, she could see. So it had better be at once, and quickly.

'There was an accident,' she said, repeating a lesson. 'My husband was taking Debby with him to pay a call on a friend. They hadn't gone more than two miles before they were hit by another car. It wasn't my husband's fault at all, but he and Debby were killed. And I was at home,' her voice, she noticed, no longer faltered, 'making Debby a new dress.'

'God rest them!' Miss O'Riordan ejaculated. 'That's a terrible thing. The world's full of sadness, my dear, but it's an ill wind, you know. With that experience, you'll be the greatest help with my orphans. Much better than Kitty who's never yet got to her first kiss.'

In the driving mirror Cathleen could see Kitty's face flaming. Did Miss O'Riordan mean to be deliberately unkind, or was she simply a steam roller, flattening people into the most useful shape for her own ends? Even Cathleen's tragedy was now to be utilized.

'Could I live with my conscience, he said.' Miss O'Riordan was off on another exploration of her private thoughts. 'I told him my conscience was as much my own affair as my stomach and liver were, and they were all in good working order. Let him look to his own, I said.'

'Aunt Tilly, who are you talking about?'

Aunt Tilly gave one of Kitty's hands a sharp slap.

'It's none of your business. I can't recount all my quarrels to you. I'm a famous quarreller, Mrs. Lamb. I draw the line only at being cursed. That, I confess, I find distressing, especially from someone to whom I've behaved generously.'

'You mean the workman at the orphanage, Miss O'Riordan?' Cathleen had taken her cue from Kitty, and realized that the old lady expected replies to her statements, even if one got one's hands slapped, like a child, for one's efforts.

'Yes, I do. He'd take the roof off the poor children's heads. "I must have more money," he said. "Or I'll leave the rain to pour in." And then he has the nerve to blame it on my conscience! What do you think of that!'

For no reason at all, Cathleen was thinking of the words in that carelessly dropped letter this morning.

You can't kill the golden goose . . . The fantastic thought had come to her that they might have referred to Miss O'Riordan. But that was making the long arm of coincidence too long altogether. There were three million people in Ireland, and no doubt a great many of them indulged in passionate quarrels. They were a warm-hearted, passionate race. Take Miss O'Riordan alone, with her generous interest in orphans. She was willing to go to endless trouble for them, and even get herself cursed, though no doubt a little intervention from her priest would solve that latter problem.

Nevertheless, in spite of the view she got in the driving mirror of Aunt Tilly's long indignant face, she had the strangest feeling that the old lady was romancing, that there was no workman repairing the roof at the orphanage, that the curse had been for something else . . .

'You'd better know, Mrs. Lamb,' Miss O'Riordan went on, 'that the O'Riordan family has always been a target for gossip and scandal, and we're no more kindly treated in the twentieth century than we were in the eighteenth. That's why I want to write this family history. It will be strong meat. From Patrick O'Riordan who was hanged by the British for sedition to my own brother Patrick murdered by the Black and Tans. Quite apart from all the romantic scandals, of course. My great-grandmother eloped in her stockinged feet – lost a shoe running down the stairs. There's rich material for you. Kitty, if you persist in looking so shocked I'll send you back to the nursery where you belong. Sometimes I doubt if you're an O'Riordan at all. You're all your mother, and how Patrick could have married that wishy washy English girl – All right, child, I don't mean to hurt you. It's not your fault. I only thank heaven Liam and Rory got good Irish eyes, and not those pale blue orbs the majority of the English have.'

At that witticism Miss O'Riordan threw back her head and gave her great shout of laughter.

Cathleen couldn't help saying, 'Pale blue isn't such a common colour in England. My own eyes are green.'

'That's beside the point, Mrs. Lamb. You're not an O'Riordan.'

Nevertheless, Cathleen was aware that she was being stared at in an assessing and not completely approving way. Miss O'Riordan was having second thoughts about her new secretary. It seemed that her own personality was the only one permitted around. Other people's had to be subdued. Like Kitty's, if the undersized little creature had ever had one.

Loughneath Castle lay a short distance from the little town of Loughneath. Here the country had changed. Grey stone walls surrounded the fields, there were rocky outcrops, gorse, moorland, cloud shadows, and goats tethered on the roadside.

Gateposts topped by crouching leopards and a curving elm-bordered drive led up to the castle. The parkland and sloping lawns were beautiful, but the castle itself was a great disappointment. Only one crumbling tower remained of the original structure. The rest was Georgian, being little more than a country house built in two wings. It was not even particularly large, although Miss O'Riordan said that one wing was shut up. The tower alone gave the building its right to be called a castle.

'We're not rich,' Miss O'Riordan said. 'We have almost no servants. Mary Kate and Patsy have been with us thirty years. Otherwise we have a woman from the village, occasionally, and Kitty and I do the rest. I'll tell you, I'm looking to that book to make some money. And it will. If I haven't spent the earnings long before I've made them. I'm a great spender.' Miss O'Riordan gave her raucous laugh again, then said quite kindly, 'You've driven very well, Mrs. Lamb. You've not given me a qualm. Well, here we are, and there's Liam waiting.'

The sight of the man standing in the arched doorway made Cathleen's heart stop. For a moment he had a strange look of Jonathon.

Then she realized she was being fanciful, perhaps merely overtired, for when she came close to him there was no look of Jonathon at all, except the way his hair grew back from his high forehead in a peak. Perhaps a little in the way he smiled courteously and sympathetically.

'Aunt Tilly! Kitty! You're late. You must be tired. And I see you've brought the new secretary.'

'Well, Liam,' said Aunt Tilly briskly. 'We're not tired in the least.' She spoke for all of them indiscriminately. 'Yes, this is Mrs. Lamb. My nephew Liam, Mrs. Lamb.'

Liam held out his hand. It was obvious he wasn't going to ignore her as Rory had. His eyes were warm and interested.

'Mrs. Lamb?' The question in his voice was just discernible.

'She's a widow,' said Aunt Tilly briefly. 'Where's Patsy? Tell him to get our bags in. And I hope you told Mary Kate to put dinner back half an hour.'

'I did, Aunt Tilly.' Liam took her arm and led her down the wide hall. Here was the affection that the old lady had

22

not given Rory, nor had Rory returned. 'And you? You got all your business done?'

Miss O'Riordan shook off Liam's arm.

'I did, of course. Didn't you expect me to?'

She sank into one of the winged chairs, stretching out her legs abandonedly.

'The divil take them all! Sister Mary Martha, the orphans, the scroungers, the hangers-on. Is Rory home?'

'Hours ago,' said Liam. 'He's been hay-making.'

'He has the soul of a peasant,' Aunt Tilly said disgustedly. 'Well, what are you staring at, Mrs. Lamb?'

Cathleen had been looking with interest at the square panelled hall. The fireplace of honey-coloured marble was magnificent. So was the dark carved ceiling. But the carpets and curtains were worn, faded and threadbare, the velvet rubbed away from the chairbacks. On the walls hung three portraits of three young men. She recognized two of them, the black-browed Rory and the finer more sensitive face of Liam. Everything about Rory was a little larger than life, Cathleen thought, even the bold stare of his black eyes. But Liam looked into the distance, dreamy and introspective.

The third face was alike and yet unlike. Cathleen thought it must be that of the father of the two boys, Patrick O'Riordan who had died fighting the Black and Tans.

'That's Shamus,' said Kitty, at her side. 'My eldest brother, Shamus.'

'I didn't know you had another brother.'

'He's dead.'

All at once Cathleen was aware of the three pairs of eyes on her, Miss O'Riordan's staring beneath drooping lids, Liam's deep-set blue ones looking at her interestedly but somehow watchfully, and Kitty's enormous empty ones, the colour of rain-washed sky.

Were they all wondering what she would say because

she had just heard that a man as young and virile as Shamus was now nothing but a portrait on the wall?

But people died every day.

'He must have been – quite young,' she said.

'He was twenty-nine,' said Miss O'Riordan dispassionately. 'His death was an accident. Kitty, take Mrs. Lamb up to her room.

'I will, Aunt Tilly.'

Cathleen followed the small limping figure of Kitty up the wide polished stairs.

'Why isn't your portrait in the hall?' she asked.

Kitty paused to turn her head.

'Mine!' she said scornfully.

She resumed her limping walk, like that of a lamed bird. She said no more. The scorn in her voice had been comment enough.

The room into which she took Cathleen was at the end of a long corridor. It was a large high-ceilinged room with long windows that looked over the garden and beyond to the wild empty country, both beautiful and melancholy. But the room itself, with its sparse and worn furnishings, showed again the austerity that prevailed in the house. The brocade curtains were frayed, the matching bedspread rubbed so thin that in places it was in holes, the Chinese hand-painted wallpaper with its delicate design of birds and flowers was tarnished and faded. There was parquet flooring and one Persian rug, its colours dim. The bed of carved oak was magnificent. In it, Cathleen thought, she would feel like a banished queen.

'My room is just down the passage,' Kitty was saying. 'The bathroom's opposite. There's only hot water in the evening when Patsy has had the boiler going.'

'Thank you,' said Cathleen. 'I don't want to get lost. Tell me what the other rooms are.'

Kitty, in her expressionless way that at the moment was neither friendly nor unfriendly, went into the passage and pointed to the door at the far end.

'That's Aunt Tilly's room. It's the master bedroom. But Liam and Rory don't want it, of course. They sleep on the floor above, and there are other rooms up there, too.' Oddly, Kitty seemed to have hesitated. She went on quickly, 'The other rooms on this floor are guest rooms except the one next Aunt Tilly's where she keeps all her old clothes. We don't use the west wing at all. Mary Kate and Patsy have their own rooms next to the kitchen. I expect Aunt Tilly will want you to work mostly in the library. It's on the left of the hall. We usually have a drink there before dinner. Come down when you're ready.'

Had the dead Shamus slept in the master bedroom? Cathleen didn't know why that thought came to her. She didn't know why she felt it would give Miss Matilda O'Riordan great satisfaction to occupy the most important room in the house. She supposed Miss O'Riordan *was* Loughneath Castle, as far as she was concerned. But no doubt further acquaintance with Rory would correct that impression.

She went back into her room and presently an undersized man with a lumpy face, and wearing a tweed cap which he didn't trouble to remove indoors, came in with her bag.

'There you are, miss,' he said. 'I hope you'll be liking it here. You'll be finding it a bit quiet, maybe. Only them squawking crows. I'll take a gun to them one day, so I will. Bejasus, there's me missus calling and me not gone more'n a minute.'

He bobbed away before Cathleen had time to speak.

She unpacked quickly, and changed from her suit into a dress. She was suddenly too tired to make any great effort over dinner this evening. She almost wanted to look unattractive. She hadn't been prepared for either Liam or Rory.

She paused to look again out of the long windows over the darkening countryside. There was a misshapen tree just beyond the garden. One side must have been cut off by lightning, and now it thrust out one leafless crooked bough which was loaded to breaking-point with the crows Patsy had mentioned. They were fighting and croaking and flying in black circles as one by one they were dislodged by their jostling fellows. The air was full of their hoarse conversation.

Crows, not cats. Birds, not babies.

I've got to be happy here, Cathleen thought desperately. I've got to be amused and lifted out of myself, but I must stand apart. I mustn't get involved with this crazy family. I must go back to Ronald saying that his idea was splendid, I had a stimulating and unique summer, did a good job on the O'Riordan book, and now am a whole person again.

Liam isn't like Jonathon . . . Jonathon never loved me in the true and complete sense of being loved . . . It's only Debby I grieve for . . .

CHAPTER THREE

'HAVE I to call you Mrs. Lamb?'

That was Liam coming towards her as she went into the library. Apart from the log fire smouldering in the enormous fireplace, there was almost no light, and again Cathleen had the illusion of Jonathon in Liam's quiet deliberate voice and the way he held his head.

It was wishful thinking, of course. Or was it? Did she really want Jonathon with his unknowable tormenting qualities back?

'You can call me what you like, I expect. My name is Cathleen.'

'That's a good Irish name. Can I get you a drink? What will you have? There's just about everything here except poteen, and I'm sure Patsy could lay his hands on some of that.'

'Patsy's the little man in the tweed cap?'

'That's him. He's a soft-tongued rascal. But then we all are.' Liam gave her his gentle slightly tilted smile. His eyes were very blue, a deep exciting blue, and set rather close and deep, so that they had a look of intensity. They were a contradiction to the quietness of his voice.

'Don't trust us when we start telling you old tales,' he said. 'Especially Aunt Tilly. That book of hers will have to be carefully censored, and even then there'll be a risk of lawsuits. Well, what's it to be?'

Cathleen saw that his hand was hovering over the array of bottles on the sideboard.

'Sherry, thank you.'

'Wise girl. You intend to keep your head. You'll need to. I wonder if we can get through dinner without a squabble.'

'Who squabbles?'

'Aunt Tilly and Rory, mostly. Sometimes I join in and Kitty comes to my defence. Poor little Kitty. You've probably noticed she's the dogsbody around here.'

'What makes her lame?' Cathleen asked.

'She was born like that. Some defect in her hip.'

'Couldn't it have been operated on?'

'Probably. But we live in medieval times here, hadn't you noticed? My father would have been too busy getting ready for the next fight with the British, and my mother—' Liam stopped, seeming not to want to say more.

Cathleen said uncomfortably, 'Kitty could be attractive if she tried. It's a pity she's lost interest.'

'She never had interest. But don't worry about her. She isn't your problem. I hope you'll like being here. I'll give you a tip. Let Aunt Tilly's tantrums fly over your head. They blow themselves out like a storm. She's forgotten them in five minutes.'

Cathleen smiled. 'There was someone in Dublin who got a taste of the storm.'

Liam's eyes narrowed slightly.

'Was there? Did you see this happen?'

'No. It was over the telephone. Something about the orphanage. I gather insults passed.'

Liam laughed. 'Trust Aunt Tilly. She was probably haggling over the price of a nail. But tell me about yourself.'

'Me? Oh, I'm only your aunt's secretary, or her ghost, if you like. I can spell and I'm literate.'

'A ghost couldn't be a more inaccurate description,' he said softly and admiringly.

Cathleen turned to the fire. Don't try to make me one of the family, she wanted to say. Again something was warning her that this would be dangerous.

'I'm only here for the summer,' she said.

'You're a widow, Aunt Tilly says.'

28

'Yes.'

'I'm sorry, Cathleen. That was bad luck.'

She didn't look at him. She was afraid his eyes would hold too much sympathy. She was tired, even one glass of the golden sherry was making her lose a little of her stern self-control, and she didn't want to make this soft-voiced Irishman her confidante after five minutes' acquaintance.

'I'd rather not talk about it,' she said.

'Of course. But you're young, aren't you?'

It was a question. Cathleen had no intention of telling him her age. She said lightly.

"What do your aunt and your brother quarrel about?'

Liam shrugged. 'Lack of money, usually. We're what's known as impoverished gentry. It's not an uncommon state in Ireland. My father took practically no interest in this estate, and then he died while we were boys, so it went on being neglected. Shamus was more interested in racing and hunting while he had it, but now it's Rory's and Rory is being deadly serious about getting it back into order. Damned boring, if you ask me. There's a great shortage of ready money. Aunt Tilly wants Rory to sell off half the land. She's tired of living like a peasant, she says. But Rory intends farming the property as it should be farmed, so all the cash is poured into dreary things like machinery and fertilizers, and Aunt Tilly has to wear her ancient sables and drive an ancient car and do her own housework, more or less.'

'I don't understand. The estate is Rory's, you say, yet—'

'Yet we all expect our share? That's true. We share the income. Actually, I have my own line. I breed horses. Hunters and steeplechasers. Most of them go to English stables. I'm hoping to breed the winner of the Grand National one day. Indeed, I think I have him in the stables now. You must come down and see him.'

He smiled charmingly, and at that moment Miss O'Riordan and Kitty came in.

Miss O'Riordan's eyes stared piercingly at the two of them. Unable to stop herself, Cathleen stepped back a pace, and then was annoyed with herself, because it seemed as if she had been standing too close to Liam. And Miss O'Riordan hadn't failed to notice.

'Liam, Kitty and I could bear something to drink, too.' Her voice was sharp.

Liam smiled. He seemed amused.

'What will you have, Aunt Tilly?'

'Do I ever have anything different?'

Liam poured a large measure of Irish whisky for the old lady and she swallowed it neat. Kitty took a glass of sherry, which she sipped, then put down.

'We won't wait for Rory,' said Miss O'Riordan. 'Let's go in.'

She led the way from the library through an arched doorway into the high-ceilinged dining-room. Elaborately carved chairs stood round an immense circular table. The floor was uncovered. The faded gold curtains drawn across the long windows billowed in a draught. Over the fireplace there was a painting of a gypsy in a flat-crowned black hat, with a multi-coloured shawl draped over her magnificent shoulders. With her long nose and gleaming black eyes she could well have been an ancestor of Miss O'Riordan. But where the painted woman's guile and cunning were plain, Aunt Tilly hid hers beneath drooped eyelids. They only showed devastatingly at the most effective moments.

A short plump woman, with a round, red, ageless face and lively eyes, brought in the food. She was no doubt Mary Kate, Patsy's wife, who had once yearned uselessly for children. She stared with frank interest at Cathleen.

'The soup's cold,' Miss O'Riordan snapped.

'Is it now? Would you be blaming me, when you were so

late? And Mr Rory – ah, here he is now, the poor soul.'

'And why is he a poor soul?' demanded Miss O'Riordan.

'Working so late and all. And him in Dublin this morning and having to take a train back.'

'That will do, Mary Kate,' Miss O'Riordan said sharply. 'We haven't asked your opinion on how I spent the day. If I decided to wear something other than rags, it takes time to buy it, doesn't it? Well, Rory.'

Rory had come in and sat down without speaking. He had put on a tweed jacket and a collar and tie, but his toilet must have been hasty for his hair was still slightly wild. His face, with its high cheekbones, and strong nose, was really quite different from Liam's. It was a handsome insensitive face. The mouth was hard.

'It would have been polite if you'd joined us for a drink,' his aunt said.

His eyebrows twitched. He was obviously about to make an impatient rejoinder when he thought better of it, and said mildly enough,

'We just managed to finish the lower field before dark. Did you have a good journey?'

'Well enough. Mrs. Lamb is an expert driver.'

'Good.'

Rory hadn't deigned to look at Cathleen. He already took her presence for granted. She supposed she should have been grateful, instead of slightly piqued. It was just that one didn't care to be ignored, like a piece of furniture.

'The orphans are to come on Saturday week.'

'Oh, God!'

'Don't blaspheme like that. I shall want some money. Their train fares will amount to twenty pounds at least, and we must have an adequate supply of food. Of course, if you prefer the unfortunate little ones never to have a moment of pleasure, and if I can't have one decent dinner gown after looking like a scarecrow ever since Shamus died—'

'Aunt Tilly, I've told you. I'm short of cash.' Rory's voice had a controlled quietness.

'There's no need for you to be short of cash.'

'I am, and we'll have no argument in front of guests, if you don't mind.'

'Rory, don't evade the issue. Mrs. Lamb isn't a guest, she's my secretary, and she's neither deaf nor dumb. She can't live in this house without knowing what's going on. And another thing, I'm going to give a dinner-party. We've been asleep in this place for long enough. There's scarcely been a soul here since Shamus died.'

'That's a splendid idea, Aunt Tilly,' said Liam. 'Who's to be invited?'

'Magdalene Driscoll, for one.'

Aunt Tilly seemed to know the effect that statement would have, for she sat back, her gleaming eyes going round the table. Her long nose twitched slightly. She looked predatory and wicked.

'What, have you decided to forgive her?' Liam asked.

'Perhaps we're the ones who should be forgiven.'

'Mrs. Lamb doesn't know what we're talking about,' Liam said. 'We're being rude. We should explain to her that Magdalene was Shamus's fiancée. At least, she thought she was. But we're not a very reliable or honest family, Cathleen. Apparently Shamus already had a wife. He'd been married secretly in Dublin to a girl he wouldn't bring to the castle.'

'She was a little nobody,' Aunt Tilly interjected. 'The whole affair was unfortunate, to say the least. Magdalene was shockingly treated, thinking all the time she was going to marry Shamus. Naturally she's bitter about it.'

'Did he mean to divorce this girl?' Cathleen asked.

Aunt Tilly's formidable nose lifted higher.

'My dear, you're remarkably ignorant. Divorce is a dirty word in this country.'

32

'Then would—'

'You mean Shamus's wife would have to die, don't you?' Kitty said unexpectedly. In her childish innocent voice the words sounded unnecessarily macabre.

'That would be the only way Shamus could have married Magdalene,' Aunt Tilly said repressively.

'Young people don't die easily,' Kitty murmured. Again her innocent words seemed invested with some underlying hint.

Shamus was young, Cathleen was thinking. But he had had an accident.

What kind of accident?

Rory stood up suddenly. His face was almost as forbidding as Aunt Tilly's.

'Have your dinner-party, if you must. Bring a hundred orphans here if you think it will get you into heaven. But stop asking me for money, Aunt Tilly. I haven't got it. After the harvest I'll spare as much as I can. But for now you'll have to make do.'

Aunt Tilly, too, was standing up.

'Rory, this is important. I must have money. Your sister needs new things. There are wages to be paid. And look at the state of the carpets. They're disgraceful. As for the heating system—'

'The wages will be paid,' said Rory coldly. 'Kitty, I imagine, isn't going without necessities. As for the carpets, they're a great deal less important than pastures at the moment. If you're wanting luxury, Aunt Tilly, I'm sure you've one or two things left that would fetch a considerable price if you sent them to London. What about the Fabergé brooch?'

'That was my grandmother's!' Aunt Tilly screamed.

'And the thousand acres you want me to sell were my great-great-great-grandfather's. I intend them also to be my son's. Now, if you'll excuse me, I've more important things to do than talk of money.'

33

He strode through the arched doorway. His untidy black head was thrown back in a gesture of unshakeable determination.

'You see?' Liam murmured to Cathleen, 'Family small talk.'

Kitty's head hung over her plate. Aunt Tilly quite calmly continued her meal, observing:

'We shall be fourteen to dinner, counting ourselves. That's a good number. You may think I waste my time arguing with Rory, but the drip, drip, drip of water does gradually wear away stone. I shall get my own way eventually, and then we'll be able to live the way we should. When I was a young girl, Mrs. Lamb, the place was overrun with servants, and I had fifteen ball dresses. We were civilized then, not barbarians, making our own hay, dusting our own furniture! Well, Kitty. Are you going upstairs?'

'Yes, Aunt Tilly.'

'Let me know if – ' she lowered her voice, but it remained perfectly audible, – 'things aren't as usual. Mrs. Lamb!'

'Yes, Miss O'Riordan?'

'Do you feel able to write a few letters for me this evening? We must get this dinner-party organized.'

The fireworks were over. They probably weren't even fireworks, but quite normal behaviour, with no sparks of hate in anybody's eyes. Shamus's wife, hidden away secretly in Dublin (was she a shopgirl or a factory girl who would be too overawed to live in a castle?) had been pushed easily out of memory, and Magdalene, the eligible young woman who had been so badly deceived, was to be compensated by an invitation to a dinner-party where the man she had loved would be only a ghost.

The big oak bed was very comfortable, and Cathleen tired enough to sleep through any kind of strange sounds the night might bring. The tapping of an ivy branch on the window, the call of owls, the sough of the wind.

But nothing, nothing, would ever make her sleep through a baby's crying.

She was awake and sitting upright the moment it penetrated her consciousness.

She listened with held breath.

The sound went on in a curious wailing monotone as if the child were not only very young but also very feeble.

How could it be a baby, for there surely couldn't be one in the castle. Whose would it be? Not poor old Mary Kate's, despite her longing. Not forlorn Kitty's. And neither Liam nor Rory had a wife.

But Shamus had had a wife . . .

Cathleen was out of bed in a flash. She knew the sound came from within the castle, yet she went to the window to make quite sure that there was no hopeful tomcat sitting on the lawn calling to the moon.

Starlight lay over the dark trees and the shadowy hills. The air was chilly. The ivy tendrils hung still. Even the sound of crying had stopped.

Cathleen stood shivering. Had it been a dream, after all, one that lingered on after she was awake? Everything seemed unreal, the dark shape of the big bed, the faint dusty smell of the curtains, the cool of the floor beneath her bare feet.

She felt very alone, caught in her obsession and marooned in this house among strangers who indulged in their passionate quarrels in her presence.

Then she heard the sound again. A snuffling, and the low desolate crying coming from directly overhead.

If Miss O'Riordan and Rory had a compulsive need to quarrel, the sound of a baby crying for attention had just such an overpowering compulsion for her. Cathleen had pulled on her dressing-gown and was starting off down the corridor to find the staircase that led to the next floor

35

before she had time to reflect that it was none of her business, and that no doubt whoever owned the baby would be both angry and indignant at her intrusion.

She found the stairs, narrower than the ones that swept grandly up from the hall, and hurried up them. It was easy enough to follow the sound of the baby. She groped for and found light switches, and left the lights burning after her heedlessly.

Here was the same corridor as on the floor beneath. It wasn't entirely dark, because at the end a chink of light showed from a not quite closed door.

It was from that room that the sound was coming.

Cathleen tapped softly on the door, and when there was no answer except the tired whimpering, she boldly pushed open the door and went in.

It was difficult then not to make an exclamation.

There was no baby in there.

The room was dominated by a four-poster bed by which a night-light burned. In the centre of the bed, propped up by pillows, was a tiny elderly woman with tossed white hair and wide staring empty eyes. She held her hands, palms outwards, against her breast, as if in a state of perpetual astonishment.

She was a little like a caught animal, Cathleen thought, a bush baby, perhaps, with its look of constant helpless unfocused appeal. She must have seen Cathleen come in, and indeed was now staring at her, but she said nothing. She had stopped crying, however. Her silence encouraged Cathleen to go forward and speak.

'Is there anything the matter?'

A door at the back of the room opened. A young girl in a dressing-gown, with a freckled face and a look of guilt, came hurrying in.

'Now, darrlin', you've been crying again. Oh! Who are you?'

36

She had seen Cathleen standing outside the circle of the light.

'I'm sorry for coming in like this,' Cathleen said hastily. 'I'm Cathleen Lamb, Miss O'Riordan's secretary. My room is directly under this one. I thought I heard a baby crying, and came up to see.'

'Oh, it's just her, poor soul. It's the only sound she can make. I was asleep.' The girl rubbed her eyes guiltily. 'I'm supposed to wake if she makes a noise. But it doesn't make much difference. When she wants to cry, there's nothing you can do to stop her. Now, darrlin',' she bent over the little upturned face, 'you close your eyes and settle down. It's after midnight. You're disturbing the house. You're a naughty girl.'

The woman in the bed had seen Cathleen now and was staring. Her lips twitched slightly. She seemed to be trying to speak.

'Hush, love,' said the girl, 'this is only Miss O'Riordan's new secretary. You knew she was getting one. I told you.'

She turned her head and said to Cathleen, 'We don't know if she understands anything or not. The doctor thinks she doesn't, but I'm not sure. Anyway, I talk to her, to pass the time.'

'Who is she?' Cathleen asked, feeling as if she were still in her dream. She had heard Debby crying, but when she went to her it wasn't the round baby face but this strange little nightmare one that turned up from the pillow to her. She hugged her arms round herself to stop trembling, for the reality seemed almost worse that the dream.

'Didn't they tell you? She's Mrs. O'Riordan. Rory's and Liam's and Kitty's mother.'

'No one told me,' Cathleen said dazedly. 'I thought Miss O'Riordan – she seemed to *be* Loughneath Castle.'

The nurse gave a short laugh.

'She's an old terror, isn't she? I haven't been here long,

37

but they say—' She stopped, glancing at her patient, inevitably wondering how much the listening ears were taking in.

'Mrs. O'Riordan had her stroke the night Shamus died,' she said. 'That's all I know. They say she hasn't spoken since, poor lamb. Look, it's nice that you're here, but you'd better go now. I must get her settled.'

The girl was very young, and her plain, kind, freckled face was worried.

'Of course. Perhaps I could come up and talk to her sometimes.'

'You can talk to me,' said the girl in a low voice. 'I haven't been here long, but the place drives me daft. I'm not qualified, and I don't like so much responsibility. But you see I don't have to get such high wages as a qualified nurse, and the old – Miss O'Riordan – her voice dropped to a whisper, 'is mean. You'll find out. My name's Peggy Moloney. I come from Loughneath. But I'm not staying here long. I'm going to London as soon as I've saved enough.'

There was no look of Rory or Liam in that pathetic face on the pillows, but it bore an uncanny resemblance to Kitty. It had the same wide, pale blue eyes, the fine small bones, the fragility. Cathleen wondered why she felt surprise that no one had told her of the invalid upstairs. Why should they have done so? She was a very new employee and the family affairs nothing to do with her.

But even Liam in his friendly talk in the library hadn't mentioned his mother. Almost as if she were being hidden away as a shameful secret. No one had said that Shamus's death had had this tragic result.

Still feeling deeply shaken and not quite out of the grip of the nightmare, Cathleen went down the stairs on the way back to her room. She was holding up her dressing-gown watching the steps, and didn't see the tall figure at the bottom of the stairs until she almost cannoned into it.

'Steady!' said Rory. And then, 'What are you doing, Mrs. Lamb? Sleep walking?'

He was fully dressed. This put her at an added disadvantage. She liked him little enough when he ignored her, but even less now that he stared at her in her state of undress. His eyes were not angry, merely curious, and quite cold.

'I heard a disturbance upstairs,' she said. 'I went up to see what it was.'

'What kind of disturbance?'

He waited with that cool look of curiosity for her answer, as if he deliberately wanted to embarrass her.

She felt a flash of anger.

'You know very well what kind of a disturbance. It would have been more thoughtful to have warned me, and then I wouldn't have had to go and investigate.'

'Do you usually feel the need to investigate the sounds in a completely strange house?'

'When it seems to be a baby crying, yes. I have this thing—' She hadn't meant to say that.

'What thing, Mrs. Lamb?'

She had begun to tremble and couldn't stop. It was the chill of the floor on her bare feet.

'I once had a child,' she said. 'I suppose it haunts me.'

He was staring at her hard. She prayed that she wasn't going to cry. Shock and strain were conspiring against her.

'You're very young,' he said unexpectedly.

'I was married very young.' She made to move past him. 'I'm sorry I did this. It must seem like prying. Now I'd like to go back to bed.'

'You'd have to have known soon enough. I don't know why Aunt Tilly didn't tell you.'

'Why should she? I'm merely here to do a job.'

'You might as well know Aunt Tilly and my mother were never the best of friends. Let me give you a small

39

warning, Mrs. Lamb. We're all practically incandescent, you know. One more quarrel and we're very likely to go up in flames. If that sort of thing amuses you, stay. But don't get scorched by us.'

He gave a smile. It held the first flicker of friendliness.

'You look too innocent,' he said. 'You can let a baby crying hurt you. No one here's been hurt by that sort of thing for a long time. I'm telling you the truth.'

CHAPTER FOUR

'So you went up to see my sister-in-law last night.'

Cathleen faced Miss O'Riordan's long expressionless face. The heavy eyelids drooped. One of the thin fingers was tapping on her desk. It was a measured tap, like the count before a race began, or a firing-squad fired their volley.

'Yes, I did, Miss O'Riordan. I made a foolish mistake. I thought it was a baby that was crying.'

'And supposing it had been, what do you suppose we do with babies in this house? Lock them in a room and starve them?'

Cathleen held her head high.

'I can only say that after my own baby's death I've been sensitive about these things. I investigated without thinking.'

Miss O'Riordan's features relaxed.

'Well, never mind. You had to know about Cecilia sooner or later. She's a hopeless case, as you could see. We don't hide her away. One merely doesn't intrude a person as sick as that into one's daily life.'

'I understand,' said Cathleen. 'It was the shock, I expect.'

Miss O'Riordan's eyelids flew up.

'What shock?'

'Why, of finding Shamus dead that night.'

'Who told you that?'

'The nurse did. Isn't it true?'

'There's truth in it. And there's been talk enough. But you're here to work for me, not to discuss my family. I hope you'll refrain from doing that.'

'Of course, Miss O'Riordan.'

'Even in the village. I don't expect you know what a small Irish town can be, shut in on itself, full of suspicions, sins, inhibitions. Oh, they'll make a scandal out of Paddy being seen carrying wood in for his neighbour's wife, and Himself away at Galway market, or Bridget tiptoeing home down that long straight street after midnight, with every house's ears quivering. So you can imagine the shenanigans that must go on in a castle!'

Cathleen laughed.

'I do understand, Miss O'Riordan.'

'I hope you do. Because I want you to go into the village later on and post those letters we did last night, and do some shopping. You'll need office supplies. I left getting those until you arrived.'

'How do I go?'

'Walk, bless me. It's under two miles. You can do it comfortably this afternoon. I never work after lunch. I take a nap. If we stick hard at it this morning we'll cover some ground. First, you can start sorting these letters and diaries. Underline anything that seems worth preserving. There's someone called Cousin Catriona, for instance, who was a prolific letter-writer. A spinster, I'll be bound, with her finger in every pie. She had nothing else to do, I expect. They had servants falling over themselves in those days. When you come to my brother Patrick, there may be a bit of censoring required. He was rather offensive, to say the least, about the British and since I have a London publisher, we must hold our fire until we see the whites of his eyes, eh?'

Cathleen found the task completely absorbing. Miss O'Riordan left her to attend to other matters, and the hours slipped by. Ireland of the nineteenth century, fiery, loyal, quarrelsome, superstitious, romantic and most of the time starving, unfolded before her eyes.

The material was rich and profuse. There were at least half a dozen novels in these letters, not the least the torn one which looked as if it had been meant to be destroyed, but then cautiously – or incautiously – had not. It simply said, '*My dearest girl, you must have been bewitched, or under the influence of Patsy's poteen. You're talking nonsense, and I deny every word. See what you can do about that.*'

It was signed simply '*Michael*', and across the bottom, in the thick-stroked writing that Cathleen already recognized as Miss O'Riordan's, was scrawled, '*The black-hearted liar!*'

Cathleen was learning caution. She had that letter tucked out of sight when Miss O'Riordan, quite unselfconscious about the incongruity of a duster tied round her aristocratic head, returned.

'That's better, that's better!' she said, flopping into a chair in one of her awkward attitudes, her long stick-like legs thrust out at right angles. 'Sister Mary Martha talked sense for once. The orphans' outing is arranged. I must send off a cheque. Well, how's your work going?'

'Very well, Miss O'Riordan. There's wonderful material here.'

'Good, good! So now you're enthusiastic. At first you didn't think an old woman like me had the material for a book, did you? I was being humoured, for the chance of spending the summer in a castle in Galway.'

Cathleeen met the snapping eyes.

'Perhaps, Miss O'Riordan. I really didn't think—'

'Very well, very well. I can see that you're going to be invaluable. Your technique and my inspiration. But I don't like secretiveness, Mrs. Lamb. Don't conceal other things from me.'

Cathleen recognized the warning. She wasn't to stumble on anything and not report it.

She set out cheerfully for her walk to the village that afternoon. Half-way there Peggy Moloney on a bicycle caught up with her and dismounted to walk beside her.

'It's my afternoon off,' she said. 'Mam likes me to go home, so I do, since I won't be in these parts much longer. Tell me what London's like, Mrs. Lamb?'

'Well – it's a wonderful place for the rich, but not so good for the poor. You'll find far more ugly grey streets there than here.'

'At least it can't be so dull,' Peggy said cheerfully. 'Everyone here has to make up scandal, if there isn't any, just to have something to talk about. You've no idea the supposing that goes on, and before long everyone thinks it's true.'

'Such as what?' Cathleen asked.

'Well, poor Mrs. O'Riordan's stroke, for instance. Did it happen because she found Shamus dead, or did he fall and bang his head when he caught his foot in the carpet rushing to her as she collapsed? Those carpets were in a shocking state, it's true.'

Cathleen had been telling herself that she knew all the secrets, but she hadn't yet heard how Shamus had met his accidental death.

'Why – doesn't anyone know what happened?'

'Not exactly. Mary Kate said she'd heard thumps, and when she went up to see what it was all about there she found them both unconscious on the floor. Wasn't it a desperate thing? Mrs. O'Riordan never spoke again and poor Shamus had struck his head on the corner of the desk when he tripped, and he died the next day from a fractured skull without recovering consciousness. And him only twenty-nine and engaged to be married, and yet his real wife there that very night.'

'The night he died!' Cathleen exclaimed.

'So they say. A young girl came to the castle asking to see Shamus, saying he was her husband. Mary Kate didn't believe a word of it – she thought she was just a saucy red-head – but she told her to wait in the billiard room until

Shamus came in. Miss O'Riordan was out somewhere, and she didn't want to bother Mrs. O'Riordan and Kitty, she thought it would upset them. So she left the girl there and went off to tell Patsy. She was away for a while, because Patsy was in the glasshouse. When she came back Shamus had come in and gone into the billiard room, so Mary Kate thought it wasn't her business to interrupt them. She went back downstairs, and it was some time after that she heard the bumps. That's all anyone knows.'

'Where were Rory and Liam that night?' Cathleen couldn't help asking.

'Liam was down at the stables with a mare who was foaling, and Rory got home late. He said he'd been into Galway.'

'And the girl?'

'Miss O'Riordan and Liam went to Dublin later on to look up the marriage register. The entry was there, plain enough. Who'd have thought Shamus would have been such a scoundrel, and him asking Magdalene Driscoll to marry him. Do you think he was planning to get rid of that red-head?'

'Is that what they say in the village?'

'Oh, they say all sorts of things. The black brothers, the O'Riordan boys were called. Sure, and you could expect any kind of shenanigans from them.'

'Do you think that girl saw what happened in the billiard room?' Cathleen asked involuntarily.

'Yes, that's what people asked. Some say she saw and was so scared she ran away and has never been seen since. Others say Miss O'Riordan pays her to stay away. There's even a rumour lately—'

Peggy stopped, biting her lips.

'What?' Cathleen asked.

'Mam said I wasn't to repeat that one. She said it was wicked.'

'Oh, all right. If you'd rather not. I expect I'll hear it, anyway.'

Peggy turned her young earnest face to Cathleen.

'You will, and all, if you go to Loughneath. It's a horrid place, everyone whispering, the men in doorways, the women behind lace curtains, everyone peeping out to see who comes and who goes, making up stories, lies.'

'I'd rather hear the rumour from you than from gossiping old men,' Cathleen said.

'All right. I'll tell you. They say Shamus's wife had a baby, and of course it's the heir to the castle, there's an entail, you see. But it's being kept hidden. Taken from its mother and her kept quiet because if she talked the baby's life would be in danger.'

The cold breath was stirring in Cathleen's heart again. Although what Peggy had just told her was a shocking surprise, yet it didn't surprise her. She had had that strange intuition all the time about a baby, thinking she heard it crying, almost feeling its presence. Yet it must be imagination. There surely could be no baby, only the ghost of little Debby.

'It must be a lie,' Peggy was going on. 'I know Miss O'Riordan could be an old devil about it, but not Liam and Rory. Can you imagine Liam wanting to hide a baby or its mother? Or even Rory, although it would mean Rory would lose the estate. He'd be the one who had reason to hide the baby.'

Cathleen found herself remembering Rory's face extra-ordinarily clearly, and the way he had looked at her last night on the staircase. He hadn't been particularly friendly, but she felt hotly angry that such a libellous statement could be made about him. She didn't begin to understand her anger.

'Couldn't the baby's birth be checked just as the marriage was?'

'They do say there's nothing recorded because Shamus tricked his wife and kept the birth a secret.' Peggy was looking anxious. 'You won't be telling Miss O'Riordan I gossiped, will you, Mrs. Lamb?'

'Of course I won't.'

'You'd hear soon enough, anyway, if you talk to people in Loughneath. Where do you have to go there?'

'To the post office, and then to buy typewriter ribbons and so on.'

'If you're wanting tea, Mam would be glad to make you a cup.'

'Thank you, Peggy. That's very kind. But I don't think I'd better be away too long.'

Much as she liked Peggy with her young guileless face, she wanted to get away from her now to digest that disturbing information. It was not only terrible to think that a baby might be callously used, but that Rory should be connected with such a crime was strangely unbearable.

'One thing,' said Peggy vigorously as she turned to mount her bicycle, 'I wouldn't believe for a minute that that baby is around these parts.'

This was another shock.

'Do they say it is?'

'Some do. But we're supposed to be all crazy in this country, didn't you ever know?'

Loughneath was exactly as Peggy had described it, a low-roofed grey town of one long winding street. Small dark shops and flat-faced houses, like a line of spectators at a procession, were on either side of the narrow road. A few cars and one donkey with its small square cart were parked outside the single hotel which was called the Brian Boru. As Cathleen walked down the street she noticed a curtain pulled sharply back, and a face disappear into the gloom. Elderly men wearing the everlasting cloth cap stared at her from doorways. A couple of little girls bouncing their ball against a wall stopped and gazed.

She was not only a stranger in this little town, but already word would have gone round that she came from the castle. She would therefore be the subject of delighted speculation. Was she really Miss O'Riordan's secretary? Was she the friend of Liam or Rory? Or even Shamus's missing wife?

At the end of the street there was a small plaque set in the stone wall. It was carved into the shape of a puckish smiling face, and bore the inscription that in the year 1718 one Sean O'Halloran had been stoned to death for using unconventional methods of healing. There was a strong smell of sheep. This small square, Cathleen realized, was probably the market place.

It all fitted in with the furtive faces behind lace curtains, the whispering about a lost baby up at the castle, the tales of violence or imagined violence. This was a town where they had stoned an innocent purveyor of medicine to death. The stain obviously lingered.

Two priests, one grey-haired and inquisitive, the other bland and smiling, paused in their stroll to glance at Cathleen. With deliberation, Cathleen walked down the street under their gaze into the uninviting hotel, the Brian Boru.

A frosted glass door led into the bar, and at it Rory O'Riordan was standing.

The opportunity to prove or disprove Peggy's story was being offered her more promptly than she was prepared for.

'Well, Mrs. Lamb,' said Rory pleasantly, 'in need of something better than Mary Kate's abominable coffee? What will you have? Our national drink?'

He waved a glass of brown liquid covered in yellow froth. Cathleen thought that it looked revolting.

'Could I have whisky?'

'By all means. Scotch, I presume?'

'If you're suggesting I don't like Irish things, that isn't true.'

'I didn't say it was. Don't be so aggressive.'

'I'm supposed to be shopping,' Cathleen said. 'I only came in here because—' She hesitated, wondering how to tell him Peggy's preposterous story.

'You're looking for local colour? You thought Ireland would be full of leprechauns and whimsical little men telling tall stories, and you're disappointed. You've found only the O'Riordans.'

'They're not exactly dull,' Cathleen murmured. She was aware that the woman behind the bar washing glasses had a stillness about her that suggested she was listening avidly to every word, no doubt to be repeated in the town afterwards.

'Anyway, I thought you were busy with the haymaking.'

'We finished this morning. I'm on my way to Galway. I'll drop you back at the castle first. Why didn't you bring the Rolls?'

'It's scarcely far enough.'

'You mean Aunt Tilly told you to walk. She's becoming a miser. Tell me—'

He stopped. His black eyes brooded. He had changed his mind and didn't intend to say anything more.

Cathleen was both intrigued and piqued.

'Yes, Mr. O'Riordan. There was something you wanted to ask me?'

He grinned suddenly. He had turned on a young and irresistible charm, like a light. It was so unexpected that it had the effect of making Cathleen completely distrust him, although her heart bumped with treacherous pleasure.

'Only quite personal things, and there's time for that. Run along and do your shopping and I'll take you home.'

He was hurrying her. Was he afraid of what she might hear if she lingered in this town? Was he the kind of man who would deliberately keep a child out of its inheritance? She looked at him and just didn't know.

CHAPTER FIVE

THE little shaggy donkey stood placidly asleep in the shafts of his cart – a tinker's cart, for it was loaded with pots and pans and bits of junk that looked entirely useless to all but the most thrifty and ingenious person. Rory's car was parked next to it.

Cathleen got in, expecting Rory to appear at any moment. She could hear someone whistling an old Irish ballad. Where had she heard it before?

She remembered at once. It had been in the streets of Dublin. Someone had been singing the song, but when she had gone up to the beggar on the bridge over the Liffey she had found that he didn't sing, he merely played his creaky accordion.

> There's a colleen fair as may,
> For a year and for a day . . .
> I have sought by every means
> her hand to gain . . .

The whistling stopped. A dark face appeared inside the car so suddenly that Cathleen jumped.

'Will ye ever buy one of my pots, lady? Or a nice shiny kettle?'

The man was as shaggy as his donkey. His hair hung over his forehead. His brilliant dark eyes gleamed. He was smiling ingratiatingly, but strangely he seemed to be laughing.

He was the man who had done the same thing to her outside the hotel in Dublin. His hair seemed longer and untidier, the handkerchief knotted round his neck dirtier. But she was certain he was the same man.

'You've had a long journey,' she said.

The man stared blankly.

'Only since dawn, lady. From the bog in Connemara.'

A donkey with its little mincing steps, like a stout lady in high heels, couldn't have come a hundred miles from Dublin in twenty-four hours. Perhaps all tinkers looked alike . . .

'Only two and sixpence for a fine kettle, lady.'

'What the devil are you doing!' came Rory's angry voice. 'Take your head out of my car.'

The man continued to smile as he withdrew. Again Cathleen thought she must be fanciful, or else the tinkers in Ireland were in a state of revolt against those who drove cars. For in spite of his smiling lips, there was a look of hate in the man's gleaming eyes.

'A safe journey to you, please God.'

His fawning voice didn't betray any other feeling. As he walked away he began to sing softly, *And if 'tis heaven's decree that mine she may not be . . .*'

He had a fine tenor voice. It was a pleasure to listen to it. As Rory backed his car out Cathleen craned back to see the tinker swing a leg over the side of the little cart and whip up his sleepy donkey. They were much too far off now to see, but she thought he was still smiling.

'Have you seen him before?' Cathleen asked Rory.

'Not that I know of. All tinkers and gypsies look alike to me, black-faced rogues.'

'He looked at you as if he hated you.'

'He probably did. I gave him short shrift.'

'No, a more personal dislike.'

'Why not? I have a car, he has a donkey. Well, what else did you discover?'

Cathleen looked at him in surprise.

'Why, nothing?'

'Don't tell me you haven't been discovering things all day.'

'What makes you say that?'

'I have the feeling that you're an inquisitive person. Didn't you begin by exploring in the middle of the night? In a strange house you had to look for a crying baby which, even if you had found it, had nothing to do with you. And I don't really think you wanted that whisky, you know. You thought the locals might gossip to you, knowing you came from the castle. Now you're cross-examining me about a tinker whom I've never seen in my life, imagining he has some personal hate for me.' He looked at her keenly. 'Am I wrong about all this?'

'As it happens,' said Cathleen coolly, 'you're absolutely right. But if you don't like me talking to anybody, you must be afraid of what I'll hear.'

He laughed with perfect good temper.

'I don't care what the devil you hear. You'll no doubt find we're all murderers before you're done. But I won't have anyone who lives at the castle joining in idle village gossip. You might have heard of the Irishman's marvellous ability to embroider a story with phantasy. So if they're saying that I stood by and witnessed my brother Shamus's death, or even assisted it, don't believe a word of it!'

'But you weren't there that night. You were in Galway.'

'So I was. And do you believe that, Mrs. Lamb?'

Cathleen looked into his face which was suddenly taut and angry. It must be that his story had been questioned and suspected.

'How should I know what to believe? I don't even know you. And it's not my business, as you pointed out. But I'm telling you here and now – ' Cathleen clenched her hands, '– if I hear any more rumours about a baby unfairly treated or in danger I shall do my utmost to find out if they're true. I mean it.' She was almost crying. She had to get over this emotional state of identifying every baby with Debby. Her compulsive search was for a ghost. 'I'm sorry if I've seemed rude and inquisitive. I only want to be assured that these rumours are false.'

Rory had slowed the car, and they were driving at a crawl down the narrow road with its stone walls that were strips of dull grey across the green fields.

'Rumours about a baby,' he said in a low voice, and she had the astounded feeling that this was the first time he had heard them. Which meant that they must be very new because no rumour in Loughneath could surely go for long unheard by everyone.

'Never mind your social duty, Mrs. Lamb. Tell me what you heard.'

'Just that your brother Shamus's wife might have had a baby. In which case—'

'In which case it – and it's a boy, of course, don't let's deny the scandal-mongers that satisfaction – will be the heir to Loughneath under the entail. Well now, what do you make of that?'

He was recovering himself. But she was sure he had had a moment of cold shock. That there might be such a child? Or that the rumour had begun?

'Do you really believe,' he went on, 'that any mother would keep such an important child out of sight?'

'No, I don't. Unless she was forced to.'

He gave a short bark of laughter.

'Now we really are getting into the realms of melodrama. So the mother is being bribed—'

'Or threatened.'

'And you think I might know something about this?' His voice held no trace of its previous good humour. It was hard and angry.

'I'm only telling you what's being said in the village. And I didn't want to hear it, if you must know!'

'But why am I being blamed for this fictitious crime?'

'I suppose, because you're the obvious person.'

He had swung the car into the drive.

'Yes. I see that. Because of Shamus's death Loughneath castle is mine. I believe I'd stop short at murder, but I'd do a great deal to keep it. Now make of that what you will.'

He stopped the car on the sweep of gravel outside the front door. Scarcely pausing to open Cathleen's door for her, he went striding inside calling, 'Mary Kate! Where's my aunt?'

He was taking the rumour up to Aunt Tilly. He was putting on a fine pretence of being startled and indignant. Cathleen looked after him, willing his attitude to be genuine.

'Well,' said Liam beside her, 'how did you persuade my brother to be civil enough to give you a lift?'

He didn't want me gossiping in the village, Cathleen was on the verge of saying. She checked herself.

'We were both having a drink in the Brian Boru.'

Liam smiled at her. He was dressed in riding clothes. There was a vague look of Aunt Tilly about the length of his face, but in no other way. Aunt Tilly didn't have those bright interested eyes, or that particularly intimate smile.

'I hope you'll let me take you to a more attractive place than the Brian Boru one evening. Will you come down to the stables and see my horses?'

'I'd love to. But I must do some work just now. I've been away long enough.'

'Aunt Tilly wouldn't mind. I know the secret of managing her.'

He very probably did, with that soft way of talking, but Rory didn't. Cathleen could imagine the old lady, wakened from her afternoon nap to hear the latest outrageous scandal.

'A rumour in the village. It upset me, too.' She bit her lip. 'I can't stand the thought of this lost baby.'

Liam put his hand on her arm.

'What rumour?' There was an edge to his voice.

55

'Do you mean you haven't heard it either? About this child of Shamus's that is supposed to be hidden away. Isn't it an impossible story?'

Liam's reaction was entirely opposite to Rory's. He simply put his head back and laughed. But only after the dark flicker of some private thought had shown in his eyes. An infinitesimal unreadable flicker.

'Would you believe it? What will they think of next to say about us? So poor Shamus lies dead for three years before they discover that such a situation would be highly intriguing, and provide pub gossip for months to come. Cathleen, my dear, you must get to know the Irish.'

'Then you don't believe it?' Cathleen said with relief.

'Good God, no. Rory's ruthless, but not that ruthless.'

'He was upset about it,' Cathleen said. She had to admit Liam's light-hearted enjoyment of the situation eased her own tension.

'He takes himself too seriously,' Liam answered. 'If you ask me, being the owner of this estate is more of a burden than a pleasure to him. He acts as if he's guilty.'

'Guilty?'

'Just in a manner of speaking. Shamus is dead, he's alive. He wants a more light-hearted approach to things. Don't you agree? Look here, you can take half an hour off to see my horses. I'll fix it with Aunt Tilly. Come along.'

Not unwillingly, Cathleen let herself be persuaded. After Rory's tenseness and suspicion, Liam was easy. She enjoyed him taking her arm in a friendly way, and walking her down to the old grey stone stables, where the two handsome colts and the filly put their heads out of their loose-boxes to look with interest at their visitors. There was a smell of fresh straw and the pungent smell of horses.

Liam told her the youngsters' breeding. He had particular hopes for the oldest colt, which he expected to sell at a high price in Dublin shortly.

'I'm not selling the filly,' he said. 'I intend to keep her for breeding. I'm breaking her in now. She's very gentle. Do you ride?'

'I had a pony once.'

'Macushla is as easy as a pony. I ride her sire, Red Rover. He's a bit of a brute, but he lets me handle him. Come and see him.'

Liam opened another loose box, and Cathleen drew back as the stallion snorted and reared inside. He was a splendid creature, his neck arched high, his chestnut coat gleaming. Liam fondled him and he was quiet at once.

'No airs, Red, if you don't mind. This is a friend. We'll be taking her riding. That's the good fellow.'

For a moment it seemed to Cathleen that Liam's gentleness had gone and he was a match for the stallion, taut, highly-bred, nervous, strong.

Then he sauntered out, closing the door, and said, 'You look very pretty standing there,' and kissed her.

She drew back more sharply than she had drawn back from the rearing stallion.

Liam still held her, but now at arms' length.

'Didn't you like me doing that?'

'No. I didn't.'

She hoped her voice was quite steady. She hadn't been kissed since Jonathon had died. Her emotions were too confused for her to understand her aversion.

'I'm sorry. We'll try again, another time.' He looked at her sideways, his eyes very bright. 'That's a promise.'

He held her hand all the way back to the house. She didn't object to that. Her fingers curled within his quite contentedly. Yet under her skin that aversion lingered. Was she afraid of new emotions?

In one of the upstairs windows a face was looking down. Cathleen noticed it only because at their approach there was a sharp movement of the curtains. Like the watchers in Loughneath, peering at her furtively.

It was Kitty. She had caught just a fleeting glimpse of her face.

Lonely Kitty. Liam was her favourite brother. If he fell in love she was afraid she would lose him. Already, apprehension was making her an enemy.

Cathleen took her hand away from Liam's. Rory was right. She had come here to work. She mustn't get involved.

CHAPTER SIX

APART from her visit to Mrs. O'Riordan's room in the night, Cathleen had kept to the rooms she had been shown. But that evening something made her go to the billiard room where Shamus had met his accident.

With its billiard table, its leather armchairs and hunting trophies, it was a masculine and curiously attractive room. There were leopard skins, one magnificent tiger skin and sundry weapons on the walls, a hunting scene over the fireplace. The floor was bare except for a sheepskin rug in front of a dying fire. The treacherous carpet had been taken up, and the desk pushed against a wall.

Cathleen walked slowly across the floor, reflecting.

'What are you doing? Looking for bloodstains?' came Mary Kate's sharp voice, making her start.

'No. I only wondered—' Cathleen looked at Mary Kate's little round figure and felt foolish. 'There's a fire. Who uses this room?'

'Mr. Rory does. He always did, as well as Mr. Shamus. And Mr. Liam. It would be the natural place for me to ask the young lady to wait that night, wouldn't it?' She had accurately read Cathleen's thoughts. 'Seeing her business was with the men.'

'But I thought it was only Shamus she wanted.'

Mary Kate nodded. 'It was.' She made no effort to correct her mistake, and Cathleen was left wondering whether it had been deliberate. Or not a mistake at all.

Mary Kate's faded eyes, a milky colour in the apple red of her face, were bland and guileless.

'I saw you coming in here, miss. I came to warn you.'

'Warn me?'

'Mr. Rory doesn't like women in this room. Not even his sister. He does his accounts here and he reads of a winter's evening.'

In other words, it was his escape route. And why not, if he wanted it?

'What was she like?' she asked impulsively.

Mary Kate pursed her lips and seemed about to refuse to reply. She knew well enough whom Cathleen meant. But the fascination of that eventful night was too much for her.

'She was a pale little thing. Seemed scared. She was dressed in a green coat, not at all stylish, and her hair was like a bonfire. You had to turn and look at it. And underneath was her pale face and her scared eyes. I knew that whatever she was up to, she hadn't wanted to come. Then I never did see her go. She might have been a fairy, do you know, vanished into thin air. But Paddy Ryan from the cabin down at the crossroads did say he saw a young thing waiting for a bus. He said she was sitting on the bench there crying. I don't know the truth of it. Plenty of girls might shed a tear, having to go home alone from a dance. And there was a dance in Loughneath that night. But that's the spot the Dublin bus goes by.'

Mary Kate clasped her hands on her plump stomach.

'I think of that poor young thing sitting in the starlight crying. She didn't deserve to come to any harm, of that I'm sure. But no mortal seems to have set eyes on her again.'

'And now they say there's a baby,' Cathleen said involuntarily.

'Aye, and they say men are flying to the moon. Look at me, miss! Do I look a strong healthy woman?'

Cathleen agreed.

'Then if you're telling me that bit of a creature, like as if she was made out of moonlight and bog flowers, could have

60

a baby, why couldn't I? It's pure nonsense, miss, and don't you go repeating wicked rumours.'

But Mary Kate was prejudiced. And the passing of time had coloured her imagination. She was almost convinced the castle had been visited by a fairy that night. Or perhaps she didn't want to believe anything else. Shamus had died, and it would be easier for a devout woman to blame the fairies than God.

Cathleen herself found a logical enough explanation. The girl was early in pregnancy and that had made her look pale and ill. She had decided the time had come for the secrecy about her marriage to end, and that had been the reason for her visit to the castle. If she were carrying the heir to Loughneath, then she must demand her rightful place. But what had happened to make the poor little thing run away and sit and cry at a bus stop on a lonely road?

The baby would most likely be a red-head . . .

Cathleen wanted to work after dinner. She hadn't enjoyed the uneasy meal, with Rory silent and Liam restless and talkative, almost as if he had had too much to drink. As well he may have, for he and Aunt Tilly seemed to have been in the library close in talk for some time when she had joined them. There was a high flush in Aunt Tilly's cheeks, too, and she was almost as talkative as Liam. But Kitty looked as if she had been crying.

Nothing was said about the subject that must have been uppermost in all their minds. Aunt Tilly told some long involved story about a priest called Father Flannigan, and Liam talked about the chances he had of getting good prices for his two colts, of Cathleen riding Macushla and of his intensive training scheme for Red.

It was good to escape to the library and work alone. There was so much material that finally she sat on the floor, spreading the letters and clippings about her.

As Miss O'Riordan had said, the past history of the family was fascinating, almost as fascinating as this story at present of a lost wife and an unacknowledged heir. There was Oonagh O'Riordan, the one who had eloped with a British army officer, losing one shoe on the stairs as she ran out of the house to her lover, and the two of them risking being peppered with shot by her furious father. In a crisis, it seemed to be automatic to an O'Riordan to pick up a weapon. The shoe, her elder sister wrote cryptically to a friend, was being preserved for posterity. '*But let us hope our family in years to come grows less reckless and hot-tempered* . . .'

There were clippings from newspapers of fiery and provocative letters written by Patrick, the boys' father, on all kinds of subjects, and one touching note on pale blue paper '*Everyone is calling you "that wild Irishman" and warning me of all kinds of dangers. I think they see you in a draughty baronial hall with wolfhounds snarling at your feet, but I see you as the only man I'll ever love. I would do anything in the world for you.*' It was signed Cecilia and the postmark was Sussex, England.

There was also a picture postcard with a Brighton postmark. It had a view of the Royal pavilion, and it was addressed to Masters Shamus and Rory O'Riordan. It said only, '*Hope you are being good boys while your Aunt Tilly and I are away. The sea air is doing me good, but the doctor says I must stay a little longer. I will have a surprise for you when I come home. Love and kisses, Mummy.*'

Cathleen wondered briefly how Cecilia, that poor speechless timid-looking woman upstairs, had enjoyed a holiday with her domineering sister-in-law who doubtless had added various rules of her own to supplement the doctor's. But obviously the holiday in her native air had restored her health, for she had borne her husband two more children since then, Liam and Kitty.

It was getting a little chilly in the shadowy room. Cathleen remembered the fire in the billiard room and suddenly thought of Rory there, alone.

The door opened and she started. Someone had picked up the telephone on the table just inside the door. She was on the floor and invisible behind the large desk. There was only one light on. Whoever was at the telephone must naturally have thought the room empty.

It was an awkward moment. She didn't want to bob up and say, 'Hi, if that's private, I'm here.'

She heard the man's low voice. Whose? Rory's or Liam's? In that low tone it was impossible to distinguish the speaker's identity. A number in Loughneath was asked for.

Cathleen's hesitation in announcing her presence had now committed her to eavesdrop. She raised herself to see the tall figure at the other end of the long room. He hadn't switched on another light and stood in shadow. The spare body and dark head could have been either Liam's or Rory's. So, too, the low furious voice as someone answered his call.

'Look here, what the devil are you up to? Have you gone mad? I'll see you at the usual time and place. I'm not letting you down, but just remember, if you let me down,' the voice sank warningly, 'I can have clever ideas, too.'

The receiver slammed down. The man strode out. Cathleen scrambled to her feet, her heart beating madly. Was it Rory? She had to know.

She went swiftly to the door, hoping to catch a glimpse of him in the hall or on the stairs.

She almost collided with Kitty who seemed to have materialized out of space and who stood blocking the door, her face white, her hands pressed to her mouth as if suppressing a scream.

'Kitty! What's the matter?'

'I saw a rat.' She shivered violently. 'I can't bear rats. They make me sick.'

There were footsteps sounding up the stairs.

'But someone just came down here. Rory or Liam. He'd have seen the rat if there was one.'

Kitty's hands fell to her sides.

'I didn't see anyone. Only the rat. It went behind those curtains. I'll have to tell Patsy.' She began to move away. 'I'm sorry. I suppose you think I'm a baby.'

'I don't at all. I'm terrified of rats.'

Kitty must have heard the sympathy in Cathleen's voice, for she paused, her wide shocked eyes for a fraction of time full of unguarded appeal. Cathleen had just time to realize that she was very frightened, and about something that was not a rat, then the veil dropped again.

'Liam had a little too much to drink tonight. He went to bed an hour ago. It must have been Rory you heard.'

CHAPTER SEVEN

THERE was a knock on her door at seven o'clock the next morning.

'Cathleen! Come for a ride.'

She was certain as to the identity of the voice this time. She stirred sleepily.

'Oh, Liam! So early!'

'It's a wonderful morning. I'll meet you at the stables in ten minutes.'

'Will your aunt mind? I'm here to work.'

'Don't you have a trade union that says so many hours work, so many hours play? I'd like to take care of your play hours. I'd make them happy.' His voice was gay and confident. It bore no relation to the threatening one on the telephone last night.

Jonathon had said, 'You would make me happy,' not, 'I would make you happy.' This, with Liam, wasn't the same at all. How, she wondered, would it be with Rory?

But the morning, soft and misty, was too beautiful to spoil by worrying. The ride across the bottom field and up into the woods took all thoughts but enjoyment out of Cathleen's head. Liam rode Red Rover, the big chestnut stallion. He looked splendid on a horse, slim, erect, completely master of his mount. He was slighter and perhaps two inches shorter than Rory which probably gave him his gentler, more diffident air when he was in the house. But here he was in his element. Cathleen, on the well-mannered Macushla, didn't attempt to compete with him.

Walking back from the stables, however, something had to be said.

'That was just what I needed to clear my head. I worked late in the library last night.'

'My head needed clearing for a different reason,' Liam answered easily. 'Aunt Tilly had me tasting the wine for the dinner-party.'

He didn't give the slightest sign that he had made a telephone call which he wouldn't have wanted to be overheard. His story tallied with Kitty's. So it had been Rory, as she had been afraid. She shivered a little. She was overheated and the wind was chilly.

'I'm finding your family history fascinating,' she said.

'Are you? I'm surprised Aunt Tilly lets you read all that old stuff.'

'Why? Is it very secret?'

'Every family has secrets. Didn't yours?'

Cathleen thought of her pleasant uneventful childhood in a large Victorian house near Salisbury, of the well-ordered lives of her mother and father, good-mannered untemperamental people who almost certainly didn't have the smallest bone of a skeleton in their cupboards. It had been a dull childhood, perhaps. It had left her unprepared for the tragedy that had struck her.

'My father was a country solicitor,' she said. 'Very correct.'

'Ah, no illegitimate babies in his life.'

'Illegitimate!'

'Wrong word. Phantasmagorical, then.'

So he had been concerned about the rumour which he had seemed to dismiss. He even went on to talk about it.

'Someone hates Rory, I imagine.'

'Who?'

'Maybe the girl, Shamus's wife. I don't suppose she meant to disappear forever. No woman is as self-sacrificing as that.'

'Then why doesn't she just come and produce the baby?'

'Well,' Liam's eyes glinted humorously, 'that could be too straightforward a thing to do. We're a devious race. We never tell the truth, for one thing. It's much more amusing not to. Try to get Rory to tell you the truth.'

'Does he know it?'

'And would I be knowing?' Liam asked, so dryly that Cathleen couldn't help laughing, and letting her apprehensions fly away.

At breakfast she was surprised to see a letter by her plate. It must be from Ronald Gault. So far, she hadn't let other friends know her address.

The postmark was Galway.

She tore open the cheap envelope and took out the thin slip of paper. It was a letter that had no beginning and no end. It was simply a clumsily printed message.

IF YOU ARE WRITING A FAMILY HISTORY OF THE O'RIORDANS YOU OUGHT TO KNOW IT INCLUDES A CRIME WORSE THAN MURDER? ASK ABOUT THE CHILD. IT ISN'T FAR AWAY. IT'S A WICKED SHAME.

Liam was at the sideboard pouring coffee. No one else was in the dining-room.

Cathleen hardly knew what made her stuff the paper and envelope into her pocket out of sight. She was only sure that she didn't want to talk about the note until she had digested it.

An anonymous letter! And she being used as a pawn in this queer mystery. At first, indignation made her want to tear up the note and refuse to be involved in something that was no concern of hers. But she knew she couldn't forget it. Whoever had written must have known, too, of her terrible vulnerability towards children.

Who in these parts knew her name? Peggy Moloney

must have mentioned it when she was home yesterday. So that now all of Loughneath knew it, the old men in tweed caps, the women behind the prim lace curtains.

'Hi!' said Liam. 'Where have you gone? I asked you if you wanted black or white coffee?'

'Oh, black, please.'

'And what else? Sausages, bacon, eggs? You can't just sip coffee after a ride like that. Tomorrow we'll go right up to the lake.'

'Lake?'

'Oh, yes, we have a tame lake of our own. Have you ever seen the blue bog-pools in Connemara? This lake is the same colour when the sun shines. Gentian. Like a jewel. The trouble with this place, it's too big. We can't control the poachers and gypsies.'

The tinker with the brown-black face, Cathleen remembered. With his persistence about selling her one of his kettles or pots, and his haunting songs.

'Tinkers, too?' she asked.

'Probably, although they keep more to the outskirts of the towns. They've got to sell their wares.'

'Do they all look alike?'

'How do you mean?'

'Rather dirty and impertinent, and burnt black with living out in all weathers.'

'And drunk, you could add,' said Liam.

'Didn't gypsies used to steal babies?'

He looked at her keenly.

'That's strictly fairy-tale stuff now. Are you thinking about that crazy rumour?'

'No,' said Cathleen, for Kitty had just come in, with a murmured good morning, and a glance under her lashes at the two of them.

'I'll teach you our local customs,' said Liam. 'Hullo, Kitty. How's mother?'

68

'Just the same. I don't think Mrs. Lamb would find our local customs particularly interesting.'

'Depends entirely on who teaches them to her,' said Liam, grinning. 'Sorry, Kit. Can I get you some coffee? You look a bit tired this morning. Didn't you sleep?'

Kitty looked at her plate.

'I'm all right. With Aunt Tilly busy on that book, there's more housework for me. And now we're having this dinner-party someone has to get the place looking presentable. I suppose you thought, Mrs. Lamb, that living in a castle there would be a footman behind each chair. It would be no use anyone holding us up to ransom. They'd get a cheque that bounced.'

Cathleen didn't miss the implication of Kitty's last remark, but she didn't begin to understand it.

After that Rory and Aunt Tilly came in. Rory was pre-occupied and said nothing. Cathleen thought that Aunt Tilly glanced sharply and expectantly through her letters, but after tearing them open she visibly relaxed, and beaming with unexpected goodwill said, 'Not a single bill this morning. Isn't that splendid! Well, Mrs. Lamb. Are you ready for a hard day's work, because I am.'

Cathleen felt as if the crumpled note were visible through the silk of her blouse. Was she to display it or not? How serious was it? Did helping the missing child depend on secrecy? She doubted her ability to concentrate on old love letters or any kind of letters that morning.

As it happened, Aunt Tilly was constantly interrupted by the telephone ringing. The people who had been invited to dinner were telephoning to accept.

Aunt Tilly had long breezy conversations with them all, and when the telephone rang for the fifth time she said, 'Now that will be Colonel Green, and he's the last.'

But it wasn't Colonel Green. Cathleen heard the changed note in Aunt Tilly's voice immediately.

She said, 'Who?' and then, sharply, 'This is Loughneath Castle. Yes. I said Loughneath Castle. You have the wrong number.'

She put the receiver down with an emphatic click.

'Damn fools!' she muttered.

A moment later the telephone rang again.

'Good heavens! I'll never get any work done. This is absurd. Why don't we have a butler to answer this?'

'Shall I?' said Cathleen.

'No. Stay where you are.'

She picked up the receiver again.

'Yes? Who are you this time? *Who?*' There was a long silence. Miss O'Riordan had turned away. Cathleen could see the white of her knuckles as she gripped the receiver. Then she said quite calmly, 'If you have a complaint to make, I haven't time to talk about it now. Ring me at three this afternoon.'

She slammed down the receiver.

'Fool!' she muttered again. 'Bothering me with trivialities.'

Cathleen wondered if it were her imagination that the old lady had gone very pale. Her skin had a waxen tinge at any time. Certainly her eyes were glittering, but they did that on very little provocation.

'Is it something I can assist you with?' Cathleen asked.

'Mind your own business!' Belatedly she apologized, 'I'm sorry. I'm beginning to talk to you as if you were one of the family. You can thank your lucky stars you're not, unless you're cleverer than I am at fending off creditors.' She began to pace up and down, a thin tall figure, scarecrowish in a loose tweed jacket with a sagging tweed skirt. 'Rory will have to do something about money. This is too humiliating. I need at least a thousand—' She swung round on Cathleen. 'What's the most we can hope for from that publisher an an advance?'

'We haven't even begun the book.'

'But there is a book. You've got to admit that. Roger Casement once stayed here. And a long time ago a young man with a big nose called Arthur Wellesley who later won the Battle of Waterloo. Isn't material like that worth a large advance?'

'We must write some of it first,' Cathleen said.

'Yes, yes, I suppose so. Then it must be Rory, the skinflint. Or one of my pieces of jewellery. By the way, Mrs. Lamb, you ride very well.'

Cathleen hadn't imagined the windows of the castle wouldn't have had eyes that morning.

'Thank you, Miss O'Riordan.'

'My nephew Liam will admire that. But don't take him seriously. He's a great flirt.'

'Is he?'

Miss O'Riordan's eyes narrowed.

'I hope I didn't make the mistake of thinking you were plainer than you are. There's nothing like a man talking flattering nonsense to make a young woman's eyes sparkle, of course.'

'You needn't have any worries, Miss O'Riordan.'

'Ho, I'm not worried. My boys have never had any admiration for English girls. They were too aware of the mistake their father made.'

(The English girl Cecilia who had written, '*I would do anything in the world for you . . .*')

'All right, I can see you think that remark was in bad taste, with poor Cecilia lying helpless upstairs. But it was true enough, and I see no reason for pretending anything else.'

'Miss O'Riordan!' Cathleen could no longer help asking the question. 'Do you think there could be any truth in this rumour about a baby?'

'A baby!' The old lady spoke the word as if it were

foreign to her, as if she had never heard of such an object before. 'Oh, I suppose you mean that impossible nonsense about Shamus's wife. Rory came home with it yesterday. He was furious. Understandably so. What will they say about us next?' She stared at Cathleen as if she, too, were the kind of object she had never seen before. 'Indeed I don't believe it. You must know that if I did I would go to any lengths to prove it. No one would be more delighted than I if Shamus had an heir. It would do my nephew Rory a great deal of good.' Her eyes glinted. 'Indeed, I'd enjoy to see the day. But it isn't true. So I'll ask you to be good enough never to mention the subject again. Ignore such malicious nonsense.'

She was a remarkable person. With this fine display of indignation she had cleverly covered her disturbed feelings. But if she would really enjoy seeing a son of Shamus's – and this seemed true – what were these mysterious threats being made to her?

Cathleen thoughtfully felt the letter in her pocket and said no more.

Oddly enough Kitty was being much more friendly. Perhaps it was because Cathleen hadn't laughed at her over the rat last night.

After lunch she said, 'Aunt Tilly never works in the afternoon, and I know she doesn't expect you to. Would you like me to take you anywhere? We could go for a drive, if you like.'

'That's very kind of you.' There was only one thought in Cathleen's mind. The anonymous letter and the existence of the child.

She didn't tell Kitty about the letter. Kitty's frail shoulders were not built for the weight of alarming secrets. Besides – had that rat last night really existed?

But someone some time would have to know about the letter. She thought rapidly.

72

'I'd love to go for a drive and you can tell me about the people in these parts.'

If the child wasn't far away it must have been brought here recently. Was it hidden, or boldly in the open?

'I suppose there isn't much coming and going, like there is in cities. People are born and die here?'

'Some of them go abroad, to England or America. Otherwise they stay here.' Kitty was watching Cathleen curiously.

'It was just this rumour about a baby,' Cathleen said frankly. 'Your aunt says it's a myth and how could it be otherwise, but I can't get it out of my mind. You would know if there were a new child in these parts, wouldn't you?'

Kitty was always pale. It was probably imagination that she had gone paler, but now she didn't look at Cathleen. She said unhappily, 'I hate gossip. We've always had to put up with it, especially since Shamus died. It isn't fair that it's started again.'

'But it hasn't any foundation, has it?'

'How *could* it have?'

'Then there isn't any new child in these parts?'

'Only the one belonging to the hairdresser,' Kitty said unwillingly. 'That's the woman who's taken the cottage at the back of the hotel and started a business.'

'How long has she been here?'

'A few weeks. Her husband's supposed to be abroad.'

'I need a hair-do,' said Cathleen. 'Let's go and see her.'

'You mean so that you can ask her questions?'

'Not exactly. Just to take a look at her. And I really do need a hair-do.'

Kitty looked at the neat upward swirl of Cathleen's blonde hair and was suspicious and sulky again.

'I don't see that it's any of your business.'

'I know it isn't. But, Kitty, try to understand this.

Ever since I lost Debby, I get this awful compulsive thing, even about a child crying in the street. I see Debby in every one of them, crying for me, perhaps, crying for some lostness.' Her eyes filled with tears. 'I can't help it. I know it's crazy.'

'Even if Shamus had had a child,' Kitty said, more kindly, 'Why should you think it's being ill-treated?'

'I don't know.' (I don't know why I must, I must, find out whether Rory is involved!) 'I just don't know, Kitty.' She wiped her eyes. 'I guess I just have an obsession. But let's go and see this hairdresser.' She tried to speak more lightly. 'You might like to get a new hair style, too.'

'Why?' That was the old prickly Kitty, a more comfortable one than the one who couldn't look at Cathleen for fear of what she would show in her eyes.

'Because you have beautiful hair,' Cathleen said simply.

Today the sun was shining, and the bleak little town looked washed with light and pleasingly austere. The old men lurking in doorways stared as usual, but touched their caps. Cathleen knew that the courtesy was for Kitty, and the curiosity for her.

Was it one of these lounging men who had sent her that note, the one who had been at the end of that brief sinister telephone call last evening?

They left the car outside the Brian Boru and walked down to the cottage. There was a notice EILEEN BURKE, *Beauty Specialist, Hairdressing*, hanging on the knob. A young woman dressed in a red cardigan and tweed skirt came to the door. She wore a quantity of heavy beads and dangling ear-rings. She had black hair and light hazel eyes. She was attractive in a sharp alive way, her thin lips smiling, her eyes observant.

It was obvious that Kitty meant to say nothing. Cathleen said easily, 'We'd like to make appointments.'

'Of course. Come in.'

She took them into a small room equipped with one washbasin, a hair drier, a shelf of bottles of lotion and shampoo, and a pile of tattered magazines on a table.

'Excuse the makeshift look of the place,' she said. 'I haven't had time to get it fixed up yet. I've only been here a month. But I have all sorts of plans.'

'What made you come here?' Cathleen asked. 'It's a very small town.'

'I don't mind it being small. I have connections around here.'

'Who?' That was Kitty, lured into speaking.

'Oh, you wouldn't be knowing them. In Galway city, and Connemara. It's nice to be near them while my husband's abroad. He's an engineer on a construction job in India. He'll be away maybe a year. It was lonely for Tammy and me without him in Dublin so I decided to move here and do a job. I've not got many customers yet, but they'll come, I hope. I'll be glad to make appointments for you. To-morrow?'

'Some time next week,' said Cathleen, with the odd feeling that by next week she would know exactly who Mrs. Burke who lived here without her husband was. She was wondering how she could ask to see the baby when miraculously there was a bump in the next room and the child began to scream.

'Oh, excuse me! That's Tammy.'

Beads and bracelets clinking, Eileen Burke rushed into the next room. Presently she returned with a boy of about two years, or perhaps more, in her arms. He was a healthy, handsome child with luxuriant black hair and bold black eyes. The tears were still drying on his rosy cheeks. He stared at Kitty and Cathleen.

'There he is,' said his mother fondly. 'He's a bit of a handful when I'm working. Aren't you, pet? But we manage. He needs his father, of course. We both do.' She

75

sighed. 'Oh, well, we'll get him back one day, won't we, Tammy?'

Her hair was very black. It shone like a crow's wing. Hair dyes were almost infallible nowadays, Cathleen found herself thinking. That was, if a girl preferred not to be noticed for her blazing red hair. Hazel eyes went with red hair, she thought . . .

As Kitty got into the car she said, almost triumphantly, 'Well, we didn't get far there, did we? I suppose now you think that woman's husband isn't in India at all.'

'I don't see why he shouldn't be,' Cathleen said evenly. 'I'd always heard that a great many of the Irish go abroad to work.'

'Perhaps they do.' Kitty was being deliberately non-committal. 'But we're wasting our time here.'

Cathleen regretted bringing Kitty on this expedition. She had thought the girl might be as anxious as she was to discover the truth, but the opposite had happened. Kitty would cover up anything she found. She was on her family's side, not the child's. If there was a child . . . *I can have clever ideas, too*, someone, last night, had been told. Was the child just a brilliant invention, a threat?

'I suppose you're thinking,' said Kitty, 'that that baby of Mrs. Burke's could have been Rory's.'

'Why Rory's?' Cathleen demanded. 'Why not Shamus's? The boy could have been older than he looked. If it comes to that, why not Liam's?'

'I think you ought to keep out of this,' Kitty said in a troubled voice. 'I don't like it. And Aunt Tilly would be furious if she knew what we've been doing.'

'Then why did you come with me?'

She didn't need Kitty's evasive answer. She suddenly knew that Kitty's friendliness was because it would be a good thing to keep an eye on Cathleen's activities after last night and the overheard telephone conversation. She had simply been strung along. Eileen Burke was a perfectly innocent new arrival, and Kitty knew it. Kitty was an O'Riordan and the family had to be protected. But if there was no child, there was some other reason for this pattern of uneasiness and suspicion.

'Shall we go home?' she said wearily, giving in.

She started the car and began to drive slowly down the narrow street. Half-way down opposite the hotel, she heard the tune of an old song whistled in clear pure notes.

> And if not mine, dear girl,
> My snowy-breasted pearl . . .

Abruptly she pulled in to the side of the road and stopped the car.

'Why are you stopping?' Kitty demanded.

Cathleen looked up and down the street. There was no sign of any whistler, no sign of the tinker with his donkey cart. Some children skittered across the street, kicking a piece of wood. A very old bent man in a doorway sucked at his pipe and stared.

'I thought I heard something.'

A window curtain moved furtively. A Cadillac slid suddenly into sight, pulled up outside the hotel and spilled out several noisy young people. For a moment the whistling sounded again, farther away.

How could she wonder at anyone knowing her name and where she lived when she was always watched?

CHAPTER EIGHT

CATHLEEN went up to see Mrs. O'Riordan that evening.

'How is she?' she asked Peggy Moloney.

'Fine,' said Peggy cheerfully. 'Aren't you, love?'

The face on the pillow was a travesty of Kitty's, the empty eyes huge in the wasted cheeks.

'Kitty and I have been into Loughneath,' Cathleen said. 'Kitty had some shopping to do.'

'See anybody?' Peggy asked chattily.

'Yes. The new hairdresser. She's pretty, isn't she?'

'And looked on with great suspicion,' said Peggy.

'Suspicion?'

'There's rumours she has callers at night. So is there really a husband in India, they say. Sure, and they'll always talk. But why would she want to come from Dublin to a place like this, with two donkeys and six bicycles!'

'She said she had connections about here.'

'I wouldn't know about that,' said Peggy. 'I haven't heard of any Burkes, though if it's in Galway she's meaning that's a city.'

'I suppose they talk about me, too,' said Cathleen casually.

'Oh, sure. Anyone new here is talked about, upwards, downward, sideways and all. Why would Miss O'Riordan be wanting a secretary after all this time? And the O'Riordans owing money here and there. Wouldn't it be a more honest thing to pay the butcher?'

Peggy clapped her hand over her mouth, looking sideways at the unmoving head on the pillow.

'I shouldn't have said that. I think she listens. But I expect she knows all about butchers' bills.'

'What else do they say about me?' Cathleen persisted.

'Why, that you have a good Irish name and all. I think she wants you to talk to her,' said Peggy. 'She enjoys seeing a fresh face.'

This was probably a too hopeful interpretation on Peggy's part. All the same, when Cathleen sat by the bed, it did seem that a flicker of intelligence came into the little lost face.

'I come from Wiltshire, Mrs. O'Riordan,' she said. 'I believe you came from Sussex. I came across the postcard you sent your little boys from Brighton. Do you remember that? You must have been ill, because you said you couldn't come back until the doctor let you.'

Now she was certain a flicker had passed over the quiet face. The eyes were still and yet seemed to have moved. She was listening, Cathleen was convinced. She began to wonder if she could invent some kind of question and answer language. Then one could ask her if Shamus had ever talked to her of his wife, ever told her she was a grandmother.

'Do you think,' said Cathleen, speaking slowly and earnestly, 'you could move your eyes slightly to the right like this,' she moved her own, 'if you mean yes, and to the left if you mean no?'

'What are you doing?' whispered Peggy. 'The doctor said she wasn't to be excited by trying to respond.'

'Did he?' said Cathleen, looking at her.

'Well, that's what Miss O'Riordan said. I was specially told not to try to stimulate her. If she caught you doing this – though I must say it seems reasonable to me to try to do something to bring her back a little.'

Cathleen bent over the patient once more.

'Did you hear me, Mrs. O'Riordan? I think there are things you'd like to tell us. Move your eyes to the right if you understand me.'

It might have been chance, but it seemed that the enlarged and startled eyes moved ever so slightly.

'Mrs. Lamb!' It was Miss O'Riordan in the doorway. In her black dress she looked at least eight feet tall. Her eyes were sparking. 'What do you think you're doing?'

Cathleen straightened herself and faced the old woman coolly. Let her scare Kitty and Peggy and all the rest with her bluster. She refused to be intimidated. What was Miss O'Riordan, anyway, an old maid with a sour temper and a secret liking for cruelty.

'I think Mrs. O'Riordan can hear what we say,' she said quietly.

'Then all the more reason not to chatter in front of her, and disturb her. Absolute quiet, the doctor said. Nurse, I'm surprised at you allowing this.'

Peggy bravely stuck to her conviction and said that she agreed with Cathleen that the patient could understand what was said to her.

'It's only kindness to bring her back into the world a small bit, Miss O'Riordan. It must be awful lonely where she is.'

The woman in the bed gave her faint whimpering cry. Now Cathleen was certain it was a signal of some kind.

'H'mm,' said Aunt Tilly loudly. 'So you call that intelligence. You know, don't you, that you might as well try to talk to a new-born baby. But if you stick to this theory, nurse, then all the more reason for consulting me as to what visitors she may have. From now on no one but Kitty will come in here without my permission. Do you understand?'

'Not Mr. Rory or Mr. Liam?' Peggy asked.

'Do they ever come?'

'Mr. Rory does. I think she watches for him.'

Aunt Tilly frowned. She probably knew the girls realized that any orders she gave would have little effect on Rory. She didn't intend to look foolish in front of them.

'I can't forbid her own son to visit her. But I expect

either you or Kitty to be here at the same time to see that she isn't excited and upset. Mrs. Lamb, if you've finished gossiping perhaps I may have a little of your time.'

All day Rory had been elusive and he didn't come in to dinner that night. Had he been keeping the appointment made by telephone last night? Cathleen was determined to see him before she went to bed. Mary Kate said he had come in late and she had given him a meal on a tray in the billiard room. Cathleen went there to find him. At her knock he called,

'Come in. You don't have to knock in this house,' he said when he saw her. 'What do you want?'

He was sitting at the desk which was covered with papers. He looked annoyed at her interruption, and was honest enough not to hide his annoyance.

'Did you know,' she said, 'that your mother can hear?'

He stared at her keenly.

'I've suspected that for a long time. Why are you telling me?'

'I think it might be possible to communicate with her.'

'I doubt it. I've tried often enough.'

Cathleen thought of that dark impatient face bending over the frail helpless one upstairs.

'Perhaps you make her nervous,' she said. 'Perhaps you remind her too much of your brother.'

'Shamus?' He was frowning. 'What exactly do you mean?'

'If she saw him die, it would be very distressing for her, perhaps more than she can work out in her present state.' Cathleen spoke earnestly. 'But she might be able to respond to someone outside the family whom she trusted.'

'Would I be wrong in thinking, Mrs. Lamb,' he drawled, 'that you are referring to that someone being yourself?'

'I wasn't, actually, but if I can help—'

She had touched him on a raw spot.

'You mean, if you can ferret out more information!

81

You've been here for two days and you've never stopped behaving like Miss Scotland Yard. What, for heaven's sake, are we and our murky – undeniably murky – affairs to you?'

Cathleen stood with her head high, holding her temper. 'I had this letter today.' She hadn't intended to show it to him, but now the anger he made her feel resulted in her thrusting the folded paper at him. 'Read it. You'll see that whether I want to or not, I'm being dragged into your affairs.'

He was frowning again, his head bent as he studied the scrawled message.

'What would *you* do about such a thing?' Cathleen asked impatiently. 'Decide it wasn't your business? Ignore it? Let a helpless child be in danger? Or go to the police?'

'Good heavens, no police! This will be settled inside the family. It's a family matter.'

How would it be settled, if no one knew what it was?

Cathleen shook her head slowly, but all she could say, in baffled anger, was, 'For goodness sake, call me Cathleen. Liam does.'

He stood up. He was really quite a lot taller than Liam. Her head would come – she took a step backwards, aware that she had flushed and that he was looking at her curiously.

'But I'm not Liam. Am I?'

'You're not Liam, in the least.'

'Good. It's as well to have that point established. Thank you for thinking it your duty to tell me about my mother. I assume you've told Liam, too.'

'Peggy said it was always you who went up to see her.'

She tried not to waver beneath his intent regard.

'Can I ask you what you intend to do about that letter?'

'No. You cannot. And I ask you to let it alone. You and

my bird-brained sister – what might have been kept inside the family is now all over Loughneath.'

So he knew about that, too.

'But we only went and made appointments with the hairdresser. Surely that was innocent enough.'

'Kitty has never had her hair done in the village. Everyone knows that.'

'Well, I warned you!' Cathleen said heatedly. 'I couldn't let a thing like a child in trouble—'

He interrupted in a quiet voice of weary boredom, 'Mrs. Lamb – Cathleen – mavoureen, if you like it in Irish – could you possibly use up those admirable maternal qualities on something else? Aunt Tilly's orphans, if you like. But just something else.'

She stood staring at him, making no move to go, thinking desperately that she must know the truth about him.

'I'm not going to apologize for interfering,' she said stubbornly. 'Nor for using time belonging to your aunt this afternoon. After all, I worked late last night. I spread things on the floor in the library and sat behind the desk. No one knew I was there.'

His black eyes didn't flicker.

'I was the last person to go upstairs to bed.'

She couldn't tell him more plainly that she had overheard him, and that today Kitty was shadowing her. But all he did was put his hands on her shoulders and say gently,

'If you insist on being involved in our melodramas, you mustn't be so sensitive. Stop inventing scarecrows. Now go to bed.'

It was only later that she remembered she had left the letter with him. So he could destroy it and pretend it had never existed. And everyone, listening to his beguiling voice, would believe everything he said. Even she, herself . . .

She dreamed she heard the baby crying again that night. But when she woke up she was crying herself.

And it was dawn, and the crows, gathered on the crooked tree, were beginning to croak and squabble. There they sat in the unreal early dawn, threatening with their weight to break off that grotesque branch.

The tree was a scarecrow like herself, inhabited only with the black birds of sorrow . . .

CHAPTER NINE

CATHLEEN opened her eyes and saw the face floating above her.

'Liam! Oh! It's you!'

Blue sky and green fields swung dizzily as she struggled up. The face above her swam in a mist, too. Then it came clear, and she heard Rory saying, 'I'm not Liam. Sorry. What happened?'

'Macushla bolted. I couldn't hold her. Let me get up. Where's Macushla now?'

'She's all right. She's made for the stables. What does Liam think he's doing, letting you ride a half-broken filly?'

'But she's so gentle. Something must have frightened her.'

She had been riding down the slope of the field beyond the shrubbery and the lawns, when all at once Macushla had turned to a wild thing, swerving sharply to the right, and then, freed of her rider, galloping away. In the suddenness of her fall Cathleen couldn't be sure whether she had seen a flicker of white among the rhododendron bushes or not.

Rory, she noticed, wore a white shirt.

But there was Liam galloping up and leaning out of the saddle to ask what had happened.

'I had a fall,' said Cathleen. 'Macushla bolted.'

'What made Macushla bolt?' Liam looked at Rory. 'Did you see?'

'Only the filly coming home with an empty saddle. Why the devil do you let a woman ride her before she's properly broken?'

'She is properly broken,' Liam retorted. 'She must have had a fright.'

'A filly that age jumps sideways at her own shadow.' The two men's gazes were locked. It was the first time Cathleen had realized the enmity between them. Rory moved first, putting his arm across Cathleen's shoulders. 'Let's get back to the house. Cathleen needs some brandy, by the look of her.'

Cathleen put her hand to her hair. It was tumbling out of its pins on to her shoulders. She was shaken, but quite able to stand alone. The temptation to lean on Rory was pure weakness.

'I'm perfectly all right, only a bit bruised, I expect. You'd better go and see what's happened to Macushla, Liam.'

Liam had slid out of the saddle.

'Jimmy will take care of her. Are you sure you're all right?'

Now both pairs of eyes, the black and the blue, were looking at her. And in the shrubbery, had that white thing moved away?

'Of course I am,' she said impatiently. 'It's not the first toss I've ever taken.'

'How did you happen to be there?' Liam asked Rory.

'A mere coincidence,' said Rory levelly.

Was it coincidence, too, that Mary Kate was grumbling about the early morning visit of one of those good for nothing tinkers, wanting to sell her pots and pans before breakfast, and him with his foot in the doorway, as cheeky as the devil.

'Where is he now?' Cathleen asked sharply.

'Miss O'Riordan sent him on his way with a flea in his ear. Me with my good copper pans, and him wanting to sell me his rubbishing stuff. The nerve of him!'

86

Miss O'Riordan, animated from her encounter with the tinker, came briskly into breakfast with a white duster tied round her head, as if she had been at her housework for some time. And Kitty's pale blue linen dress had seen so many tubbings that now it was almost white.

The movement that had startled Macushla could have been the flash of the tinker's bright tin wares as he slipped away through the back garden.

It could have been a branch whipped with a gust of wind, or a pigeon flying out of the undergrowth.

The disarray of Cathleen's hair was noticed, and the reason had to be given. It was no use to say feebly that her typing fingers were intact. Miss O'Riordan was angry, and said bluntly that Cathleen was paid to work as her secretary, not to be entertained as if she were a guest at a country house, with morning rides and dinner-parties.

An argument began to fly about Cathleen's still dizzy head.

'Hang it, Aunt Tilly, she can't do more than an eight-hour day. She must have recreations.'

'She's welcome to read any of the books in the library, and walk about the gardens.'

'You can't make her a prisoner.'

'Prisoner, is it! And her twice in the town, already. And finding her way all over the castle. Talking to this one and that one. Oh, a great talker she is. And now, at dinner tonight, she'll be treated as a guest. I've put her next Colonel Green because of his British sympathies, the poor misguided fellow.'

Here Cathleen roused herself.

'I'm afraid, Miss O'Riordan, after that bump, my head—'

'Whatever's happened to your head is your own fault entirely. You'll come to dinner, because otherwise the numbers will be wrong. I refuse to sit down thirteen at a table. You have my permission to excuse yourself immediately afterwards. But accidents on horses aren't something I bargained for when I engaged you. I can't be put to the expense and trouble of finding another young woman with your qualifications. So I merely ask you to stop training for the Dublin Horse Show, or whatever it is, and stick to your job.'

'A dictatorship, you see,' said Rory, and Cathleen realized that he was speaking directly to her. 'Or perhaps matriarchy would be a better word.'

'And what nonsense would that be you're talking?' Aunt Tilly said icily. 'I'm not your mother. I merely struggle to run this impossible household while she's incapacitated. Where, I'd be having you tell me, would you all be without me?'

Liam got up and walked round the table to give the old lady's shoulder a squeeze.

'We all know what you've done for us, Aunt Tilly.'

A flicker crossed her long face. That was the only sign she gave that Liam's gesture had pleased her. She said in her rasping voice,

'Kitty, don't take all day over your breakfast. The silver must be cleaned, and Mary Kate won't have time to help. I want Patsy for polishing furniture. It needn't be said all over County Galway that Loughneath Castle has gone to rack and ruin. We'll have candles on the dinner-table. Their light is flattering for more than one kind of ruin.' Her eyes snapped round the table, looking for appreciation of her wit. 'Kitty, did you hear what I said?'

Kitty's hands went involuntarily to her cheeks. Had she thought this was another small verbal cruelty of her aunt's? She didn't raise her eyes.

'I'll do the silver, Aunt Tilly.'

'Good. And don't forget to pay some attention to your own appearance. I admit none of the guests are very young, but there's no point in not making the best of yourself. Colonel Green still has an eye for a woman, even if he's rather more than a day over sixty. Mrs. Lamb, if you're going to faint, don't do it here.'

Cathleen opened her eyes wide. She felt far from faint at that moment. Healthy indignation was surging through her. She knew that in this household she was never going to be able to let well alone. Kitty must have an ally.

'I'm not going to faint, Miss O'Riordan.'

'Then if you need an aspirin, go and take one. I expect you to be in the library working by nine-thirty.'

'Welcome to ould Ireland,' said Rory. He suddenly put back his head and shouted with laughter.

Miss O'Riordan was right about the candlelight. It made the room look shadowy and magnificent. The dark secret eyes of the gypsy in the painting looked down at the polished table with its crested Georgian silver and Waterford glass, at the guests in evening dress and jewels.

Contrary to Miss O'Riordan's warning, Cathleen found her neighbour, the elderly Colonel Green, a courtly and entertaining person with more than a touch of the blarney. Opposite her, Liam looked very handsome indeed. He kept giving her intimate glances which she refused to acknowledge, but which undeniably made her heart beat faster. Kitty, apart from her unfortunate red dress which completely extinguished the little colour she had, was doing her best, talking to a middle-aged couple who apparently lived for hunting. The enigmatic Magdalene, though her shining red hair swathed round her head was beautiful, was not otherwise as striking as Cathleen had expected. She sat next to Rory at the head of the table. Rory, in spite of his conventional attire, still had a touch of wildness about him. It was in his eyes, Cathleen realized. They were too bold

89

and bright ever to be subdued to the convention of a dull dinner-party.

But the evening was Miss O'Riordan's.

'She ages wonderfully,' Colonel Green said in an undertone to Cathleen. 'She's a much finer-looking woman now than she was as a girl. Then – well, what with her plain face and her temper, the young men kept well out of harm's way. Though I must admit there were scandals. Oh, yes, indeed.'

'Scandals seem to be a prerogative of this family,' Cathleen murmured.

'Always have been. Always will be. Ah yes, Miss Matilda was quite a girl.'

The candlelight shone on the long eccentric face, the piled white hair, the scrawny neck, the expensive black gown. It shone, too, on the brooch pinned at the centre of her flat bosom, and this held Cathleen's eyes irresistibly. Who, least of all Colonel Green, would have believed the scene that had taken place not an hour before.

'Mrs. Lamb, I want you to go to Dublin tomorrow. You'll have to spend the night, and return the following day.'

'Certainly, Miss O'Riordan.'

'I want you to take this brooch to a jeweller. I've telephoned him. He knows the piece very well. He will give you five hundred pounds for it.'

'Five hundred!'

Aunt Tilly's eyes raked her with magnificence and contempt.

'My dear girl, it's a Fabergé piece. It was my grandmother's. It should of course, be an heirloom, but that's less important now than the necessity for money.'

'But what a pity—'

'I didn't ask you to express an opinion, Mrs. Lamb. Worse things happened in the potato famine.'

So Cathleen could say no more. She couldn't even ask if Rory knew of this sacrifice of one of the family heirlooms which, in its way, was as significant as the land he refused to sell. She could certainly never ask why Miss O'Riordan had such an urgent need for five hundred pounds.

The gypsy in the painting wouldn't have minded losing the brooch. She would probably have preferred her multi-coloured flamboyant glass beads to diamonds and sapphires.

Colonel Green followed Cathleen's glance to the picture and whispered, 'One of Sean O'Riordan's whores. That was in the day when all the landed gentry had their whores painted.'

'Wasn't she really a gypsy?'

'Heaven knows. Could have been, at that. Wouldn't trust an O'Riordan.'

Talk of the gypsy had made Cathleen think of something else.

'Do you have tinkers calling at your house?'

'Not that I know of. My housekeeper would give them short shrift. They might poach on my property, thieves and rascals that they are.'

'Are they still illiterate?'

'I should think so. The lazy devils wouldn't waste time going to school.'

So if all tinkers were illiterate it couldn't have been the tinker who had written that note. Unless he had persuaded someone to write it for him, and then had journeyed thirty miles to Galway to post it.

But who?

Or was the persistent tinker not a genuine member of that star-light and sun-up profession?

When the ladies left the table, Cathleen contrived to walk beside Magdalene Driscoll.

'Would you like to come up to my room to powder your nose?' she asked.

She hoped Miss O'Riordan hadn't noticed. If she didn't

talk to Magdalene now the girl would be monopolized by other people, and then would be gone.

On close inspection, Magdalene was more attractive than Cathleen had at first thought. She had a sharp nose, but delicate features and an exquisite skin, also an air of great pride. She looked at Cathleen curiously.

'You're the new secretary, aren't you? Is Miss O'Riordan really writing a book? I should think she's asking for libel suits.'

'It's fascinating material.'

Cathleen watched Magdalene as she sat in front of the mirror. She saw the disillusioned eyes looking back at her from the glass.

'Fascinating is right. Up to the present day.'

'I expect you've heard the rumour, too. About the baby.'

'I gather that most people have. Someone has made it his business, or her business, to see that it spreads. At that, rumours spread of their own accord in this country.' She shrugged. 'It won't be the first illegitimate child in this family, I should think.'

'Illegitimate?'

'How else?' Magdalene had turned to face Cathleen. Her eyes had no hint of mockery. 'Shamus wasn't married, you know. Nor did he have a child.'

'But—'

'Oh, yes, you've heard all the stuff, about the marriage register, and so on. Couldn't there be another Shamus O'Riordan? It's not an absolutely unheard-of name. All I know is, it wasn't my Shamus. He didn't lie. Oh, I know what you think. That Irishmen don't lie, but speak cleverly and amusingly round the truth. Shamus didn't even do that. He was honest.'

'But the baby—'

'God knows! Ask Rory. Ask Liam. That's if it even exists.'

'I had an anonymous letter. I lost my own baby not very long ago. I suppose this person knows and is thinking I'll be sympathetic or gullible or something, and start making things awkward for the family.'

'Hell!' said Magdalene sympathetically. 'That makes two of us bereaved. I am sorry.'

'But who would write the letter to me?'

'The baby's mother, perhaps. If there is a baby. I suppose she fondly imagines she's the wronged one. But if she were honest she would come into the open, wouldn't she? There'd be no need for this back-door approach.'

'You mean that red-headed girl who came—'

'That will-o'-the-wisp, that bog fairy!' Magdalene suddenly put her face in her hands. 'I don't know. All I know is that I loved Shamus and he loved me. And now he's gone. Don't get mixed up with this family. I'm warning you. You'll only get hurt.'

'Scorched,' Cathleen murmured. 'That's what Rory said.'

'Rory's like Shamus.'

'Honest?'

'I wouldn't know about that. One honest O'Riordan in a generation would be riches. No, he's only like him in looks. I have to keep away from him. I might be tempted to do this transference of feelings thing, and find I'd an imposter on my hands. Or in my breast.' She began patting powder on her nose. 'Do you think we're all crazy?'

'So that's where you both are,' said Kitty at the door.

Neither of them knew how long she had been there. Not that it mattered. They'd said nothing she didn't know already.

No one had told Cathleen of Magdalene's conviction that Shamus had not been married. But why should they have? It wasn't her business.

'Liam's looking for you,' said Kitty. There was a red spot

in each of her cheeks. 'And Aunt Tilly will be expecting us all in the drawing-room.'

'Sure, Kitty,' said Magdalene. 'We're only gossiping. Isn't it time you untied those apron strings?'

'Apron strings?'

'Your Aunt Tilly's. She's exploiting you, the old devil. Don't tell me. I know.'

She walked to the door, giving Kitty's cheek an affectionate pat. 'Time you fell in love and kicked over the traces.'

Was that the kind of treatment that would win Kitty's confidence and affection? Looking at her stony face, Cathleen was sure it wasn't. Was there a way at all? There was, of course, for Liam had found it. But he was a man, and that was probably the secret. Poor lame Kitty, shut into herself, longed for a man's love, and automatically hated any woman who had had it.

The night was warm, so Aunt Tilly had ordered that the doors on to the terrace remain open. In that way the curtains could be drawn back and their shabbiness hidden. But she had overlooked the fact that it provided an escape route for her guests. A figure already stood out there in the darkness, smoking a cigarette. Cathleen thought it was Liam, then realized that it was Rory, for Liam was talking politely to the hunting couple. Cathleen heard him saying, 'I'm hoping to nominate Red for the Grand National if I can raise the wind.'

'I thought you were going to put him up for sale at the Dublin Horse show.'

'No, not Red. I won't part with him. We haven't had a National winner since my great-grandfather bred one. I can do as well as old Sean O'Riordan.'

He looked up and saw Cathleen. He gave her the slightest flicker of an eyelid and presently, having drawn Colonel Green into the conversation, slid away from the group and edged Cathleen towards the door.

94

'Let's get some fresh air.'

'Should we?'

'Don't I remember Aunt Tilly saying at breakfast that you might excuse yourself immediately after dinner?'

Cathleen laughed.

'So she did. But I've enjoyed the party.'

'I've enjoyed looking at you.'

They were out on the terrace, away from the splashes of light cast by the windows. Rory had disappeared. Liam took Cathleen's arm and led her across the grass to the lily pool with its dead fountain. It, like the curtains and carpets, was scarred with neglect and age, the writhing stone fishes flaking dust into the murky water.

It was romantic, nevertheless, even if it didn't splash musically as it had done for the ears of the impulsive Oonagh when, flying to the arms of her lover, she had left a high-heeled slipper to posterity. And even perhaps for the young Matilda whose sable wrap and heirloom jewels had not succeeded in finding her a husband.

'I have, you know,' Liam insisted. 'You have lovely shoulders.'

His fingers touched them. Cathleen shivered.

'Cold?' he said.

'No. Don't, Liam.' She stepped back to avoid his embrace.

'Don't you like me?'

'Yes, I do, but—'

'When I saw you this morning after that fall I wanted to knock Rory down, and take you in my arms.'

'Rory just happened to be there.'

'I know. A habit of Rory's.'

Cathleen looked at him in surprise. It was the first time she had heard bitterness in his voice. Had Rory taken other girls of his?

'As for me,' she said, 'I just don't want to get involved.'

95

'You looked beautiful tonight in the candlelight. I couldn't stop looking at you. What's wrong? Are you scared to get involved? You're too young to be a widow forever. You can't turn into a spinster like Aunt Tilly or Kitty. Let me meet you in Dublin tomorrow night.'

'You know I'm going!' Cathleen exclaimed.

'It's not a secret. Mind you,' his eyes gleamed in the darkness, 'I don't know why you're going, though at that I can make a guess. The crafty old devil is up to one of her financial transactions. She won't trust Rory or me because she doesn't want us to know how much is involved. She puts the half of it on horses, you know.'

'Really! Is that why she's always complaining of having no money?'

'And the other half she spends on making a splash like tonight, proving the O'Riordans aren't has-beens. Where can I meet you tomorrow night?'

'You can't, at all. I'd lose my job, to begin with, if your aunt got to hear about it.'

'She won't hear about it. I'll say I'm going to Athlone to look at a brood mare. Let's say the bar of the Royal Hibernian hotel at seven o'clock. There's a fountain there that really works.' He didn't attempt to kiss her this time. He merely put his hand on her arm and looked at her pleadingly. Beneath his gentleness she sensed, for the first time, an intensity, a will that was not to be shaken. What Liam O'Riordan wanted he would try very hard to get.

'I'll bring you back to life, my darling.'

His soft voice was persuasive. Jonathon's soft voice, when he wanted something, had been irresistible. The voice of a man with only self-love . . . And now Jonathon seemed so long ago.

She must be living in a dream if she thought that Liam had any more of Jonathan than a surface similarity.

She longed, yet dreaded, to come back to life.

'I'm enjoying this job, Liam. Don't spoil it for me.'

'I intend making it for you.' He had taken her warning as consent. He squeezed her arm. 'I'll be there tomorrow.'

For ten minutes she had forgotten Magdalene and that curiously distraught scene in her bedroom. But now, to change the subject and evade the intimacy Liam was forcing on her, she said casually,

'Liam, did you know that Magdalene refuses to believe Shamus was ever married?'

'Wouldn't you, in her position? A woman has to save her pride, I imagine.'

'Yes, I suppose so.'

'Aunt Tilly has her here to let bygones be bygones. But I wouldn't take too much notice of an hysterical woman.'

Wouldn't it be Magdalene, Cathleen thought, who was generously letting bygones be bygones? She certainly looked remarkably unhysterical as, later, she put on her wrap to leave. She said to Cathleen in a low voice, 'That thing we were talking about. You might investigate Miss O'Riordan's sudden craze for orphans.'

'Sudden?'

'In the last two years. She decided she needed a pet charity. Perhaps she's doing penance for something. Who knows?'

Magdalene's eyes were sharp and wicked. She had planted some more seeds of revenge. Liam was right. Her pride had made her hate the O'Riordans. She wasn't letting bygones be bygones at all.

CHAPTER TEN

It was the first time that Cathleen had been in Miss O'Riordan's bedroom, the magnificent master bedroom with its long embrasured windows that encompassed the formal gardens, the sheltering bank of shrubs, the sweep of green fields, and on the horizon the misty indigo hills of Connemara.

It wasn't right that an elderly spinster should be occupying the carved four-poster with its rich but tattered hangings, a marriage bed if ever there was one. But Miss O'Riordan in her sable wrap, and with her haughty and overbearing air made her possession indisputable.

She held out a box to Cathleen.

'Here it is. Guard it with your life.'

The melodrama was scarcely necessary. True, the brooch was an historic piece that rightly should have been sold in a famous London auction room. But one hardly expected to be attacked and robbed on the train to Dublin. Yet the far-fetched thought brought an unwelcome memory of the tinker's impertinent dark brown face thrust towards her . . .

'I'll be careful, Miss O'Riordan.'

'And by the way, Mr. O'Donnell will pay you in cash. Just a little precaution. I don't want any nosey tax officials asking questions.'

'But you'd be perfectly safe, Miss O'Riordan. This represents capital.'

'Spare me your knowledge, Mrs. Lamb. Why should the Government know I'm in the desperate position of having to dispose of valuables? Let's keep our pride, what we have left of it. Now be off or you'll miss your train. Since we

98

can't work together I intend to spend the day resting. I'm exhausted after last night. But it was quite a success, don't you agree? The O'Riordans haven't lost their touch. That claret was put down by my father. I hope Colonel Green, the old scandalmonger, didn't convince you that the gypsy in the painting was our ancestor.'

'Was she?' Cathleen asked.

'Only on the wrong side of the blanket, if so. Who knows? I sometimes think the strain comes out in Rory. And I shouldn't be surprised if I had a little of it myself. Oh, I'm a match for anyone, Mrs. Lamb. Let them try their tricks.'

Looking at the narrowed malicious eyes, Cathleen was quite prepared to believe her. But she suspected an undercurrent of strange seriousness in that last remark, almost an undercurrent of fear . . .

As well as disposing of the brooch, Cathleen knew what she intended to do in Dublin.

At three o'clock, with five hundred pounds in ten-pound notes bulging inside her bag, she went to the office of the Registrar of Births, Deaths and Marriages. She meant to see for herself the famous entry of Shamus's marriage.

When she did find it, she stared in disbelief. Shamus O'Riordan, son of Patrick and Cecilia O'Riordan of Galway to Moira Frances Regan, daughter of . . .

Cathleen scarcely saw the rest of it. The name was shouting at her. *Moira!*

The name that had been in that scrap of letter she had picked up in the Gresham Hotel on her first day in Dublin. The sentence that had said *Moira should have come to her senses before it was too late* . . .

Shamus's small lie in describing himself as a commercial traveller from Galway city, which no doubt had been meant to keep his wife away from the castle, seemed insignificant in comparison with this.

Yet, out in the cool windy sunshine, she asked herself what she was in such a fuss about. Just as Shamus was not an uncommon name in Ireland, neither was Moira.

How could she know this was the Moira to whom the letter referred? Wasn't that a too improbable coincidence?

Yet there had been the rest of it about someone deserving to be murdered, but that one couldn't kill the golden goose. In other words, the goose who paid up. And the distraught look of the man, like and yet unlike that dark-faced tinker. For how could a tinker have dressed up to go into a smart hotel and known how to behave there?

Moira . . . So that was the name of the ghost girl who had since disappeared into thin air.

The money in Cathleen's bag seemed suddenly terribly heavy. *What was it for?*

Belatedly she remembered the most important thing of all. She had meant to search the register of births over the last five years for the birth of a child to an O'Riordan.

She went back into the office and paid her fee. But this search proved fruitless. There was no son or daughter born to a Shamush O'Riordan or to a Moira Regan. She carefully checked both sources.

The baby remained as much a ghost as its mother.

She was glad she was going to meet Liam that evening. These things must be discussed. Should she take all that money back to Miss O'Riordan? Was Miss O'Riordan in danger? *Deserves to be murdered . . .* The words were burnt into her mind. If she didn't have the money (not to place surreptitious bets on race horses, but for other purposes) would she be murdered?

Cathleen had little time or inclination to take trouble over her dressing. She clasped on a pearl necklace, brushed her hair and swiftly pinned it up, retouched her make-up, noticing that she was flushed and distracted and hoping Liam wouldn't misinterpret the reason.

She was ten minutes late at the hotel, and saw that Liam was already there at the bar, his back towards her.

She rushed up to him.

'Liam!'

He turned, his black eyes full of mockery.

'Rory!' she exclaimed.

'Second time,' he drawled. 'Second disappointment?'

'You're awfully alike from the back.' That was all she could think of to say.

'What will you drink?'

'Oh – nothing, thank you. I'm waiting for Liam as now you must know.'

'I don't think so.'

'Why? What's happened?'

'Red seems to have developed a chill. He didn't want to leave him.'

'Did he send you to explain?'

Rory laughed shortly.

'Liam wouldn't send me anywhere.'

Cathleen knew that Liam wouldn't leave his most valuable horse if it were in danger. There would be a message from him at her hotel, of course. She had rushed in and out without making inquiries for messages.

But if Liam hadn't sent Rory, how had Rory known where to come at exactly that time?

'You overheard us last night!' she accused.

He grinned.

'You should choose a more private place if you don't want your assignations overheard.'

'Oh! You're impossible. First you wouldn't look at me and now you're following me. What are you up to?'

'I liked you better with your hair tumbled,' he said seriously. 'The way it was when Macushla threw you. Like this!'

She ducked from his hand.

'Don't be a fool!'

He grinned again. 'Yes, I'm following you. What did you discover at the register office?'

'Nothing you don't know already.'

'Perhaps not. But you come to it with a fresh eye, a remarkably analysing eye, if I may say so. Which is strange, for it looks so dreamy. Made for gazing on fountains and flowers, or, shall we say, a loved countenance. It doesn't look at all like the gimlet it is.'

'You make me sound like the one-eyed gorgon,' Cathleen said, without amusement. 'Don't tell me when they handed out the blarney they missed you.'

'Sure, and don't you believe it! I haven't begun yet. Well, Cathleen. Did you notice anything? I'm serious, and this is important. And I know you did. You came rushing in here, bursting with some sort of news. You can tell me, you know. Perhaps I haven't been exactly encouraging before. But I mean this.'

'You can shut me out until I'm of some use!'

'Never mind being feminine. And I still don't like your interference. But you'd better tell me. Hadn't you? And you can trust me, you know.'

'Can I?'

'Sure,' he said easily, and she was farther away than ever in knowing what to believe.

But she had to tell him because there was no one else. He listened intently and without interruption. He said the name 'Moira', softly like a caress. He had a beautiful voice when he cared to speak softly and with feeling. Probably he hadn't missed out on the blarney after all. Or had the name Moira a special meaning for him?

Then he asked her a great many questions about the drunken writer of the letter, commented that it wasn't an unusual state for a Dublin citizen, and finally said,

'I don't see how we can take it personally. Do you?

I mean, why should this thing have blown up just now? It's three years since Shamus died, and four since he married.'

'There was the day your aunt was having trouble with a workman at the orphanage,' Cathleen said irrelevantly 'We were delayed in leaving Dublin because of it.'

'What workman?'

'I don't know. Someone who apparently accused her of having no conscience.'

Rory said nothing for a full minute. Then he beckoned to a waiter and ordered more drinks. He leaned back comfortably in his chair.

'Where would you like to eat?'

'Are we going to eat?'

'Naturally. Liam's absence needn't deprive you of food.'

'I can get something back at my hotel.'

He behaved as if she hadn't spoken.

'Do you know, you look alive for the first time since I met you.'

Cathleen was very conscious of her flushed cheeks.

'You mean, it's the first time you've looked at me.'

'Don't you believe it! But you haven't lost your husband for so long, have you? You've still got him inside you, I think.'

Cathleen hadn't expected so much perception from him. It shook her badly. She wanted to say that she wasn't looking at Jonathon any longer, except in perplexity as to which one of them had failed. At last she was facing that knowledge. It was bitter and healthy. But it didn't make her equal to Rory O'Riordan's complexities.

Later in the evening, that was so different from what she had anticipated, Cathleen saw that Rory was drinking too much, and wondered if he were trying to forget the name Moira, or its owner. He had followed her to Dublin for a reason, and probably kept Liam away for the same reason.

He must have been afraid of what she would discover.

His eyes, in the dim light of the restaurant, were amazingly bright.

'Where's the money, Cathleen?'

She had thought he was going to pay her another of his satirical compliments. She hadn't expected this.

'What money?'

'That little courier job my aunt asked you to do. It was hardly fair expecting it of you, so I'll relieve you of the responsibility.'

'Don't you dare!' Cathleen held her bag tightly. 'This is her money, and I deliver it to her.'

'Good lord, I believe you think I mean to rob you.'

'How do I know what you're up to?'

Rory gave a faint amused smile.

'What am I up to? Protecting you from other thieves. Protecting Aunt Tilly from folly. Besides gaining medals in heaven just as she is. I intend to call at the Mary and Joseph Orphanage in the morning. You can either be ready to leave at eight, and wait while I see the sisters, or I'll come back for you afterwards.'

'We're not travelling together!'

'Just as you like. But I've an empty car.'

'Rory!' She leaned forward. 'I don't understand any of this.'

'Neither do I.'

'Magdalene was so certain Shamus wasn't married. You knew your brother. Would he have deceived a girl like that?'

Rory began to shake his head. Then he seemed to recollect himself and said lightly, 'An O'Riordan will deceive anyone if he's in a tight corner. Hasn't your research proved that to you? Drink up your wine and I'll take you back to your hotel.'

It was the hotel where, her first morning in Dublin, the

five cats had cried outside her window. Cathleen had looked for them on her arrival today, but they hadn't been anywhere in sight.

'The money,' said Rory softly. 'Seriously. For your peace of mind. It's too negotiable.'

The dark street was empty. No, not quite. A thin tall man slouched by, his cap pulled over his eyes. He paused at the corner, looking back, then disappeared into a doorway. Cathleen didn't think the door opened. No shaft of light showed.

'Will you take it from me, anyway?'

'I will.'

'Oh, blast you!' She took the bundle of notes from her bag and thrust them at him. 'Who's interfering now?'

'Me,' said Rory, and pulled her into his arms.

She struggled violently.

'I like you when you come to life.' His face was close to hers.

'Let me go! You – you Irish barbarian!'

'Green,' he said to himself. 'Sparking green.' And kissed her slowly and thoroughly.

'Your eyes,' he added.

'You're drunk,' Cathleen said in angry disgust.

'Not at all.' He drawled the brogue. 'Actually, that was for the benefit of the fellow on the corner. I have a small feeling he was watching us. Sure, mavoureen, you're in a hurry to leave me!'

CHAPTER ELEVEN

THE incident last night might not have happened. Cathleen sat in the car outside the bleak grey walls of the orphanage waiting for a sober and silent Rory who had done no more than bid her a brief good morning when he had picked her up. Her rehearsed cold remark, 'I'll travel with you because it's convenient, but just don't touch me,' remained unsaid. It merely seemed silly, like the behaviour of an hysterical virgin. It was evident that Rory hadn't the slightest desire to touch her.

She could hear the voices of the children. They were playing in the yard beyond the brick wall. A ball was bouncing, and there were shrill screams. They sounded like ordinary children despite the fact that they had been abandoned so early in life. She longed to see them. She knew she would search their features, as Rory no doubt was doing at this moment.

It was almost an hour before Rory returned. He apologized for keeping her waiting.

'What were you doing?'

'Talking to the sisters. The children seem happy and well-cared for.'

'Don't tell me you're turning philanthropic.'

He turned and gave her his unexpected sunny charming grin.

'Let's hear your guess as to what I was doing. I'm sure you've got a most original one.'

'I expect you were checking admissions and sponsors, or whatever orphanages require to admit a child.'

'And thereby found my long-lost nephew? Or by that look on your face, you might even be thinking it was my own son. The only admission recently, you might be interested to hear, was one Peter Brady, the youngest of a destitute family of nine, the father a drunkard, the mother on the streets. He's a bright little fellow, all the same. A mop of red hair. You like them red-haired, don't you?'

'And who was responsible for getting him in?'

'Who do you think? My tender-hearted and good Aunt Tilly. She's a great worker, God bless her. Well, Cathleen. Did you sleep well?'

That was two little boys, fatherless, or virtually fatherless. Tammy Burke and Peter Brady. What had either of them to do with the O'Riordans?

'Sleep? Oh, well enough.' She hadn't fallen asleep until long after midnight, and then had been awakened by the sudden agonized squawk of a cat. It sounded as if it had received a mortal injury, and she had sprung out of bed to look out of the window at the low roof where the cats congregated.

There was no four-legged creature in sight, but a long narrow shadow lay across the galvanized iron. Her heart had jumped violently. She had thought it had moved, and that it was a man. Then she had realized that it was bright moonlight, and a tall chimney cast the shadow.

All the same, she had closed and locked her window before going back to bed. She had been remembering the tall thin shadow that had slunk into a doorway as Rory had outrageously kissed her goodnight.

'You'll be seeing Peter Brady for yourself,' Rory said, as an afterthought. 'He's one of the lucky ones chosen for the great outing to Loughneath Castle. Does that satisfy you?'

'I don't see what it has to do with me.'

'Exactly what I've been telling you all the time.'

He wasn't being facetious any more. The sober stern look had come back to his face. He didn't start the car for a minute, but said, 'Can you bear to make another call before we leave Dublin?'

'Peter Brady's parents?'

'How did you guess?' he said ironically. 'If they're home. And sober. Sister Mary Martha gave me the address. Let's go.'

The house was in a poor street full of noisy children, dustbins, and slinking grey cats. It had dirty torn lace curtains pulled across the windows. The woman who came to the door was a slattern with a scarf tied round her head. A squalling infant inside, and her half-buttoned dress, suggested that she had been interrupted in feeding the baby.

'Are you Mrs. Brady?' asked Rory pleasantly.

'I am not. I'm Mrs. Dooley. What would you be wanting?'

'Does a family called Brady live here?'

'Not to my knowledge. Not in this street. You must have the wrong address.'

She stared inquisitively. A gaggle of children had gathered round the car. When the woman saw that Rory was not going to make any explanation she said disappointedly, 'That's my baby yelling his head off. I'll have to go back to him.' She was unbuttoning her dress as she went.

'Wrong address,' Rory said briefly, as he got into the car.

The children scattered, with little puffs of dust, a flight of bedraggled sparrows.

'Deliberately?' Cathleen asked.

'Who knows?'

'But wouldn't the sisters at the orphanage look into an admission case more fully?'

'Not,' said Rory dryly, 'if sponsored by my aunt.'

After a long time Cathleen asked the question that worried her most.

'Will your aunt be in danger?'

'How?'

'If she doesn't get the money you took from me last night.'

'You mean, because she might not be the golden goose any longer? Well, I suppose even that fabulous creature came to an end of her eggs at some time. I intend to put a stop to whatever nonsense Aunt Tilly is up to. It shouldn't be difficult. If it's blackmail, the blackmailer couldn't be more stupid, could he? Writing infantile anonymous letters. I should think he's probably a fairly harmless lunatic.'

Cathleen said the one thing that made sense to her.

'If this is all about a baby, even the possible heir to Loughneath, how can your aunt be blackmailed? What would she have to hide?'

Rory frowned. He made no answer to that.

'You would be the obvious person, wouldn't you? Someone may think you wouldn't like an heir to turn up. Or even,' she continued boldly, 'that you may be hiding him.'

'Having first murdered his mother,' said Rory levelly. 'Or do you give me credit for stopping short of murder?'

Cathleen stared ahead. After a long time she said, 'I'm sorry. You know I didn't mean a word of that.'

'Thanks.'

She moved slightly nearer to him. She didn't deserve to be forgiven. She couldn't explain how important it had been to believe that he was innocent, nor tell him of this first small flowering of trust in him.

So there was silence again while the miles slid away. At last they were back in the familiar stone wall country, and approaching Loughneath.

'Keep your eyes open,' said Rory. 'Tell me if you see the tinker.'

But the roads were empty. There was no plump donkey

and cart, no sardonic whistling man with his shiny pots and pans. At Loughneath, Rory stopped the car and leaned out to the group of old men sitting, like shabby ungroomed cats, in a sunny doorway.

'There's been a tinker around here. Have you seen him lately?'

'Not today, no sir.'

'Yesterday?'

'Yesterday morn, sir. He were going through here with a great clatter. Woke the missus!'

'Has he been in these parts long?'

'No, sir. Says he come from Connemara, but I'd be thinking he's a stranger in these parts. He bought the donkey from Paddy Doolan not three days since. Said his own had dropped dead in the shafts. He had money to pay for it, Paddy said. Paddy said he'd a mind to go tinkering himself, if money came that easy.'

'Thanks,' said Rory.

The cool fingers of fear were touching Cathleen's heart again. It had been absurd of her to think that the dark-faced man could have come all the way from Dublin in a donkey and cart. No doubt he had driven a car that was a good deal faster than Miss O'Riordan's ancient Rolls.

The grey roads winding between the grey stone walls seemed very empty . . .

Liam came out to meet them.

'Well – had a good time?' He was looking only at Cathleen. His voice was deliberately light, his eyes furious.

Rory got out of the car.

'Where's Aunt Tilly?'

'Don't ask me. In her room, I imagine.'

Rory went inside without another word. Liam looked after him, losing a little of his hostility in curiosity.

'What's the matter with him?'

'I think he has things to talk about. How's Red?'

Liam answered absently,

'He'll be all right. I dosed him up last night. What's happened? Why is Rory rushing off to Aunt Tilly like that?'

'Nothing's happened. That's just the point. It's like stabbing at a shadow. I'm glad Red's going to be all right. It would have been awful if anything had happened to him.'

Liam, aware of Cathleen's sincerity, relaxed a little.

'Thanks. You don't know how sorry I was about last night.' His face darkened again. 'I didn't know I couldn't trust my own brother.'

'We only ate together and talked about things. When I saw him I thought it was you.'

'Were you disappointed?'

'Liam, stop sticking out your lip like that. You're like a small boy.'

'I don't feel like one, I assure you. I could have killed Rory, going off like that, knowing you were mine.'

'Yours!' Cathleen exclaimed in astonishment. 'Aren't you being a little premature?'

He pulled her towards him.

'I'm not premature,' he said, kissing her hard and painfully.

She sprang away angrily, startled by her feeling of revulsion.

'I won't stand this sort of thing! I won't! Rory last night, and now you— What's wrong with you both? You act as if you've lived in a monastery.'

'I love you,' Liam said. 'I'm speaking for myself. And I won't stand you fooling about with my brother.'

'Liam, will you get this straight!' Cathleen said furiously. 'I wasn't fooling about with Rory. He was only—' she stopped, realizing that now she was about to defend Rory for his particular brand of outrageousness. She sighed, deeply and wearily.

'If you must know, we were only doing a little investigating.'

Liam watched her intently.

'What sort of investigating?'

'We called at the orphanage to see a child. At least, Rory did.'

'This wild-goose chase! What happened?'

'He was a little boy called Peter Brady. Your aunt had arranged for his admission. But whether that's his real name or not, we don't know. We couldn't find his parents. The other name, Moira—'

'Moira?'

Cathleen suddenly felt immensely tired. The whole of yesterday and today was taking on the quality of fantasy.

'Shamus's wife. I hadn't known that was her name. It's pretty, isn't it? I fancied she had something to do with the tinker, but we couldn't find him. Other days he has his head stuck in the car at every opportunity.'

'Cathleen—' Liam had come close. He looked deeply concerned. 'You're talking nonsense, do you realize? I expect you've been up most of the night, and travelling all day. That's why you're not making sense. Did you do Aunt Tilly's errand safely?'

'Oh, yes. But Rory thought he ought to take charge of the money. He told me to lock my door at the hotel. Yes, it does sound like a bad film, doesn't it?'

'Worse than that. Do you think you were wise to trust Rory so much? I certainly wouldn't have. Well, never mind. I think Kitty's making tea. You look ready for it. And Cathleen?'

'Yes?'

'Try to take me seriously.'

'I do, I assure you.' She tried to laugh. 'So much so that you worry me. I only want to be left alone.'

'Then you'll have to make that clear to Rory, too, won't you?'

'Don't worry,' she said coldly. 'I can cope.'

But could she? Now, with jealousy, as well as everything else?

Liam had disappeared when Cathleen had washed and come down to tea. There was only Kitty, serious and uncommunicative, at the table.

'Where's everyone?' Cathleen forced herself to speak brightly.

'I don't know.'

'I was talking to Liam five minutes ago.'

Kitty's eyes flickered. 'He's gone down to the stables.'

'Oh, yes. He's worried about Red. How has your mother been, and your aunt?'

'You've only been away twenty-four hours, Mrs. Lamb. Nothing much happens in that time.'

'Will your aunt be coming down to tea?'

Cathleen's mouth felt dry as she thought of trying to explain to Miss O'Riordan why Rory and not she had the money. It had been a private errand on which she had been sent, and she seemed to have messed it up completely. But had Miss O'Riordan ever tried to withstand Rory?

'I expect so,' said Kitty. 'If she isn't too upset.'

'Upset?'

'She's been quarrelling with Rory. But that's nothing unusual. Oh, here she is now.'

Miss O'Riordan came in smiling. Her long face was arranged in an expression of courteous welcome.

'Well, Mrs. Lamb. Now we'll be able to get down to work again. I hope you feel up to a late session tonight.'

'Certainly, Miss O'Riordan.'

'You didn't miss too much sleep last night?'

Her affability mystified Cathleen.

'I'm not tired at all. I'm sorry I couldn't complete the

113

errand you gave me, Miss O'Riordan. I hope I didn't do wrong—'

'Rory has explained everything, thank you, Mrs. Lamb. We must allow him his eccentricities. He's an O'Riordan, after all. What do you think, Kitty, Rory has been showing an interest in my orphanage.'

Kitty shot her a startled look.

'Don't look so disbelieving. There may be some good in your brother after all. He had a long chat with Sister Mary Martha. He even took a look at the children who will be coming on Saturday. Yes,' she wagged a long forefinger, 'I knew that would surprise you. But there's more. He gave me something towards expenses. Now what do you make of that? It must be your civilizing influence, Mrs. Lamb.'

So nothing more was to be said about the five hundred pounds, which may or may not have changed hands. Now she wasn't to know whether Miss O'Riordan had had to forgo her passion for a gamble on a horse, or not. Nor was she to know what the old lady thought of the situation. The O'Riordans obviously stood together.

There was only a minute to slip up to the sickroom before dinner.

Peggy greeted her eagerly.

'I'm sure she's been looking for you. There's been something on her mind. I can tell.'

But to Cathleen the face on the pillow showed no change. She looked down at the fragile crumpled cheeks, the eyes turned up like fading flowers. She didn't know how Peggy Moloney could guess that there was something on her patient's mind, since there seemed to be no mind at all. But suddenly it seemed unbearably frustrating that inside that brain, if only it could be revived, lay the key to the whole puzzle.

She was never to know what made her lean forward and say clearly,

'Moira! Moira Regan! Does that name mean anything to you, Mrs. O'Riordan?'

With shocking abruptness the woman in the bed began to make her whimpering cries.

'Oh, dear!' exclaimed Peggy. 'Now you've upset her. She hasn't cried all day. There, there, dearie. It's all right. It's only Mrs. Lamb. She's been to Dublin. She's had a wonderful time. Hope you did,' she added to Cathleen out of the corner of her mouth.

For no reason at all, Cathleen was thinking of Rory's kiss. Her lips seemed to burn.

'Do you think she didn't like me saying that name?'

'I doubt it would mean anything to her,' Peggy said cheerfully. 'Who was this Moira Regan, anyway?'

'She was Shamus's wife. That's if he had— Oh, never mind. I'll have to fly or Miss O'Riordan will be up, and she won't like finding me here.'

As at tea, there were only Miss O'Riordan, Kitty and Cathleen at dinner. Places were laid for the two men, but neither appeared.

Mary Kate had her usual grumble about keeping meals hot for all hours, and Miss O'Riordan said firmly,

'Indeed, and you'll not think of trying. If my nephews are late they eat cold food. That's the rule.'

As Mary Kate shuffled out with a tray of dishes, Miss O'Riordan went on,

'My nephews are never required to make explanations, Mrs. Lamb.'

Her black eyes snapped at Cathleen, daring her to ask either Rory or Liam any questions, no matter what stage her friendship might have reached. But in her very curtness, Cathleen sensed tension. Miss O'Riordan herself would dearly love to know what the men were up to. What had passed between her and Rory? What had happened to the money? Why was she behaving as if Cathleen's very confidential errand in Dublin hadn't even existed? And above all, what were Liam and Rory doing?

'Mrs. Lamb, I expect some intelligent work from you this evening.'

The old lady hadn't missed Cathleen's abstractedness. Neither had Kitty, who said slyly,

'I expect Mrs. Lamb must be tired after a late night last night.'

'A late night now and again wouldn't do you any harm either, miss.'

Kitty flushed and was effectively silenced. The uneasy meal was at last over. It was very warm. Darkness seemed to have come an hour too soon. But this was due to an incipient storm. When Cathleen went to the library she saw the magnificent black clouds piling up on the horizon. The air was heavy with the threat of thunder.

Thunderstorms didn't frighten her. On the contrary, they filled her with a strange excitement. It was difficult to concentrate on her notes as Miss O'Riordan talked.

Miss O'Riordan seemed to find it difficult, too, for she spoke jerkily, and every now and then got up to walk about the room. Her memory was faulty, and she kept repeating herself. The material was rich with drama, but tonight the flavour had gone out of it. Neither of the two women were living in the past. They both had their ears alert for a sound of the men returning. Cathleen was sure Rory was out searching for the tinker who might once, in his true colours, have written and torn up an indiscreet letter in the bar of the Gresham Hotel, and later, for she now recognized the histrionic style, have written that anonymous note to her. Liam – his sick horse couldn't have kept him all this time down at the stables.

Was there a light in Eileen Burke's window tonight? Suddenly that thought occurred to her. Eileen was sharp-eyed but attractive. She loved gaudy jewellery. She must wear it for some man.

Lightning flashed across the windows, and there was a distant crack of thunder. Miss O'Riordan peered out into the dark night.

'Kitty's frightened of storms. She gets hysterical. I'd better go up. Can you carry on alone?'

'Yes, Miss O'Riordan.'

'There's no need to stay up all night. But we must begin making progress. Something's got to happen.'

She stood, tall and gaunt, against the dark window, and Cathleen knew she wasn't referring to the book being completed, or its profits. There was something much more compelling on her mind.

After that, the house was very still. The storm seemed to have moved away, the rumble of thunder becoming fainter.

With an effort of will Cathleen returned to her work. Soon the fascination of the letters and diaries absorbed her again, and she began marking passages. It was a pity none of them were more up to date. Even Aunt Tilly's had stopped at the time when Shamus, Rory and Liam were still small children. Kitty wasn't even mentioned.

'*Entertained Patrick's junior officers. Talked of ball. Will have to organize it oneself, Cecilia incapable.*'

'*Dublin, to see caterers and order new gown.*'

'*Ball last night. A great success. Cecilia obscured in that unfortunate gown. How typically English of her to wear pale blue. For the rest, magnificent. The O'Riordans never in better form.*'

After that there were long gaps. A brief entry, '*Back from the awful appalling boredom of Brighton.*' Later still, '*Cecilia pregnant again.*' and even later, '*Liam has measles. Am nursing him myself to keep infection from others. Cecilia would go straight from sickroom to hug and kiss Shamus and Rory and the Baby. Never stops to think.*'

117

'*Patrick in skirmish with the Black and Tans. They'll get him one day, curse them.*'

'*Liam better. Determined to keep up with the bigger boys, the gallant little fellow.*'

The last entry of all was stark and brief. '*Patrick dead. They got him at last, the black murderers.*'

Apparently after that Aunt Tilly had either lost heart or grown into the kind of sober maturity that made her uninterested in the comparative trivia of a diary.

A vivid flash of lightning startled Cathleen out of her absorption. The storm was back again, and this time directly overhead, for the first crash of thunder was violent. Then the rain began. Cathleen couldn't resist throwing the windows wide open and leaning out to smell the freshness and to see the smothering black of the sky.

Lightning lit up the silent fountain, then died and the thunder crashed again. At the same moment the wind sprang up, and the castle was full of rushing draught and billowing curtains. With a brief struggle, Cathleen got the windows shut. At the same moment the lights went out.

For a second she stood still, feeling the eeriness. The room was pitch-dark, so was the hall and the staircase. Fortunately she had matches in her handbag. Pondering whether to go searching for Mary Kate and Patsy, who might produce lamps, or to grope her way up to her bedroom and go to bed, she decided on the latter course. She could undress in the dark.

She struck matches to find her way up the stairs. The ceilings looked enormously high and shadowy, the staircase disappeared into black darkness. Half-way up the match burnt out, and she stopped to light another. At the same moment she heard strangled sobs.

They came from Kitty's room, she was sure. Kitty who got hysterical in thunderstorms, particularly, one imagined, when the lights failed.

Poor little thing, thought Cathleen, and hurried to the top of the stairs, the match burning out again. It wasn't quite so dark up here. The thundercloud was passing over, for dim light came in the long window at the end of the passage, and she could see the vague shape of doorways. She groped for Kitty's door, opened it and went in.

But now there was complete silence, except for the blowing wind and the faint shush-shush of heavy curtains.

'Kitty! Are you all right?'

She put out her hand to feel the way, and encountered something tall and upright. What was it? A bedpost? A person?

Her voice shook. 'Kitty! Have you got a light?'

At that moment the lightning flashed again, brilliantly, and Cathleen's heart stopped.

She had walked into a room full of people, strange rigid people standing staring at her. There was an overpowering smell of mothballs and old clothes.

Nobody moved. Cathleen put out a hand and touched a smooth, cool cheek, a nose, coarse, lifeless hair.

She clapped her hand to her mouth, suppressing a scream.

Were all the O'Riordans in here, embalmed and standing upright? Or was she in a dream in which all those letters and diaries had come to life?

The thunder was dying away, rolling in the distance. But the flashes of lightning remained vivid and the next flash showed Cathleen that, among the standing figures, there was one sitting.

And the wind sounded like someone breathing . . .

Mesmerized, she put out her hand to touch the cold cheek of the sitting figure. And felt soft flesh . . .

Then she did scream. She snatched back her hand as if it had been burnt. There was a chuckle. The figure slowly and deliberately stood up. Against the wan light of the clearing sky Cathleen could see the silhouette of a tall person in an immense cloak.

'You deserved that fright, Mrs. Lamb,' said Miss O'Riordan in her gravelly voice. 'Poking in here, too. One of these days someone will bite that inquisitive nose of yours off.'

'This house!' gasped Cathleen.

Miss O'Riordan chuckled again. Her dress rustled as she moved. She had let the cloak slip back from her shoulders, and Cathleen could see a dim sparkle on her bosom.

'This dress might look like a million glowworms – as someone once said – but it's hardly sufficient to illuminate the room. Have you got any matches? There's a lamp over there that could be lit. I've been sitting here waiting for Mary Kate with candles. These power failures happen now and again. We're always prepared.'

Cathleen found her hand shaking too much to strike the match.

'I heard Kitty crying. I thought this was her room. I made a mistake in the dark.'

'Well, never mind,' said Miss O'Riordan pleasantly. 'I intended to show you in here one day. It'll be of use to you in the book. Here, girl, give me the matches. What did you think you'd seen? a ghost?'

Someone dead, and still sitting upright, Cathleen thought. The horror was a black shadow over her.

But in a moment Miss O'Riordan had the old-fashioned lamplight glowing, and Cathleen was able to see clearly the amazing array of figures, each dressed in a different costume.

'Preserving this museum is a little hobby of mine,' said the old lady. 'I thought what a pity it was for expensive gowns to moulder away, folded in drawers, so at great expense I had these figures made and now I preserve the more interesting things. See, here's my mother's wedding gown, these are two of her ball gowns. And here's my grandmother dressed for a race meeting on the Curragh.

Now there was a woman of spirit, and a leader of fashion in her day. And you see this.' She held out a yellowed brocade slipper with a ridiculous little high heel. 'The famous slipper, lost on the stairs.'

She picked up the lamp and moved among the still figures, an uncanny evocation of another age herself.

'If you're interested in more modern times, I've found it amusing to keep my own favourite costumes. I once had fifteen ball gowns, did I tell you? Ah, those were the days.'

'That's one you're wearing?' Cathleen asked.

'This? Yes, my favourite. It was the time when sequins were all the rage. I also happened to wear it on the happiest night of my life. So sometimes I put it on and sit here quietly reviving old memories.'

She shot her sharp glance at Cathleen.

'Do you think I'm crazy?'

'Sentimental,' Cathleen said warily, and at the same time knew that sentiment was the last emotion with which she would have credited Aunt Tilly.

'Cecilia and Kitty both think I'm crazy. But perhaps neither of them has ever had that sort of night. One can't see what sort of costume they're going to contribute to the museum. Not even a wedding dress. Cecilia didn't wear one, and Kitty—' Miss O'Riordan shrugged eloquently. 'The storm's dying. Will you go down and see what Patsy's doing about lights. Take this lamp. I'm perfectly happy in here in the dark.'

She was crazy, Cathleen thought as she left. And yet there was a shrewd sanity in the gaze she gave Cathleen. She enjoyed evoking the past in this way, and why shouldn't she.

Now she could see Kitty's door, which she had accidentally passed. No sound came from within. She hesitated, then decided it was wiser not to disturb Kitty now she was calm again.

She went on down the stairs in time to see Mary Kate bustling into the hall with lighted candles.

'Is that you, Mrs. Lamb? It's a fuse. Patsy's seeing to it. Is everything all right upstairs?'

'I haven't been up to Mrs. O'Riordan.'

'Then I'll just be slipping up to take a look. Not that the poor creature would notice even if the heavens split open and all the saints fell through. And now, who's that?'

The great front door had opened and slammed shut. In the dim light Cathleen saw Liam standing staring up at them with a strangely white face.

She ran down the stairs towards him.

'Liam! Where have you been? You're soaked.'

His black hair was flattened in streaks, drops hung on his eyelashes. His tweed jacket was dark with wet.

'I've only run up from the stables,' he said. 'I didn't realize how the rain was belting down. I got soaked just in that time.'

'You would and all,' Mary Kate said disapprovingly. 'It's a cloudburst. Why didn't you put a horse-blanket or something over you?'

'Didn't think.' Liam shook himself. 'Rain doesn't hurt anyone.'

He blinked in the dim light.

'Power failure?'

'There is. Patsy's fixing it. I'm just going up to see to your mother.'

'Liam, you look so tired,' said Cathleen.

He rubbed the water out of his eyes.

'Do I? I'm all right. Rory home?'

'I don't think so. Unless he's in the billiard room. Do you want to go and see?'

'In the dark? No, thanks.' He shivered. He must be cold. He took her hand a moment. His own was wet and chilly.

'I didn't mean to be so late. I was a bit upset after this afternoon. Do you forgive me for that?'

'That!' she said lightly.

'You don't hate me?'

'Good gracious, no.'

'Then I'll make you love me.'

'Liam, get your wet things off. Go to bed.'

'Yes. Yes, I must. Then I'll see you in the morning, darling.'

'Goodnight, Liam.'

She watched him go, a stranger with his flattened black hair and white face. He had called her darling in that intimate way as if she belonged to him. But she had the strangest feeling he had been talking to someone else who was still deeply occupying his thoughts and making him distrait.

If he had come all the way from Loughneath he could scarcely have been wetter . . .

CHAPTER TWELVE

It was very much later when Cathleen heard the sound of car wheels on gravel. Rory was home at last. Just afterwards the grandfather clock on the stairs struck three. The rain had dropped to a whisper. By dawn it had stopped.

Cathleen got up at seven to a sparkling morning. An impulse seized her. She knew that the best way to disperse the shadows of that strange day and night was to go riding across the fields and through the rain-fresh woods. She wouldn't wait for Liam. She preferred to go alone, anyway. The O'Riordans had become a little overpowering, and an escape for an hour would be refreshing. If Jimmy wasn't about the stables she would saddle Macushla herself.

The filly greeted her with nervous whickers of pleasure.

'Now, remember, no shying at ghosts today,' Cathleen said.

There was no one about. She saddled Macushla, then, before taking her out of her loose box, went to look at Red.

The big stallion snorted and reared. His coat gleamed rosily. He looked in the pink of condition.

'I don't believe you've been sick at all,' Cathleen said, talking to herself. She barred the door against the restless stamping horse, and saw Jimmy, the undersized stable boy, approaching.

'Good morning, Jimmy. Red looks none the worse today.'

The boy's eyes were still sticky with sleep. He stared at her stupidly.

'Did something happen to him, miss?'

'Didn't he have a bad chill the day before yesterday?'

'Mr. Liam was fussing, to be sure, miss. But he's always

fussing over Red. He said nothing about any chill at all.'

Cathleen hated herself for asking.

'He was worried. Wasn't he down here until late last evening?'

'I wouldn't be knowing, miss. I fed the horses and locked up round about sun-down. Then I went home. He might have worried about the storm upsetting them.'

'Yes, of course. If he comes down, tell him I've taken Macushla, will you?'

It was just one more thing to puzzle her. Liam couldn't have wanted to tell her the real reason for not meeting her in Dublin. She dismissed the thought.

At the moment she desired nothing but Macushla and the bright morning, the cool sprinkle of drops from every overhanging bough, and the green fields stretching away to the shadowy hills. She remembered something Liam had said about a small lake lying like a blue jewel beyond the woods. She would look for it. If there was no one about she might even be able to swim in it. She didn't know, apart from the fresh morning, why she suddenly felt this resurgence of life. It was hardly logical, with the frights and false alarms she had been experiencing. But she was vividly aware of her healthy body, of the soft air on her face, of what it was like to be kissed again.

In her imagination it was Liam's lips that touched hers. But it was Rory's face, brilliant and demanding, that hung over her.

Rory was a devil, Liam – here, she couldn't formulate her thoughts. For the charming and kind person she had known by no means fitted with the white, soaking and dishevelled man who had come in last night.

In what state, one wondered, had Rory returned?

The lake shone in the distance, a sapphire dropped into the fields among the rocks and the clumps of yellow gorse.

Cathleen was delighted at finding it so easily. She let

Macushla pick her way among the rocky outcrops until they reached the water's edge. Then she dismounted, looped the reins round a jutting stone, and turned to survey the landscape.

There was no one in sight. This was an utterly lonely spot. Only cloud shadows moved. And something else — what was that that tinkled faintly and metallically?

Cathleen's heart had begun to quicken even before she saw the donkey, the fat shaggy grey beast so like a small stout fussy dowager. The pots and kettles, catching the sun, hung on either side of its saddle, clashing gently as it grazed.

So she was not alone after all. The tinker was here! He must be crouched behind some bush, peering at her, no doubt waiting to see if she would decide to undress and swim. No doubt smiling his secret lewd smile in anticipation . . .

Cathleen quickly unlooped Macushla's reins. She felt near to tears, half with vexation, half with fear. She had her foot in the stirrup before a slight movement in the pool caught her eye. Just beneath the surface of the jewel-bright water there was a log — no, a fish, for its white under-belly was visible.

Not a fish! The white under-belly was — No, no, no! Cathleen screamed the words silently. It couldn't be the face of a drowned man. Bleached in the water, no longer that healthy black-brown from the winds of the open road. Floating gently just beneath the darting flight of dragonflies and midges . . .

Then Cathleen was in the saddle, and no longer letting Macushla pick her way daintily, but urging her to a gallop. There was only one vague and irrelevant thought in her head, and that was that now Paddy Doolan could have his young healthy donkey back. The tinker wouldn't be needing it any more.

126

At the door of the castle she slid off Macushla, let Patsy, who came hurrying up, take the reins, and stumbled inside.

'Miss O'Riordan! Liam! Rory! Oh, Rory!' For it was he who came quickest, and he into whose arms she fell. 'I've found the tinker.'

'Cathleen! You've had Macushla out. She's all in a lather.' Liam had come striding to the door after Rory.

'Be quiet, Liam,' said Rory. 'What is it, Cathleen?' He held her away from him, searching her distraught face. 'Where did you find this tinker?'

'In the pool. I once – caught a dead frog – without knowing it was dead. That's how – he looked!'

'What is all this?' The overpowering voice of Miss O'Riordan cut into the infinitesimal silence. 'Has Mrs. Lamb had another fall? Wasn't she told not to go riding?'

'Look after her, Aunt Tilly.' Without ceremony, Rory thrust Cathleen into one of the carved hall chairs. 'Get her some brandy. And ring the police in Galway. Are you coming, Liam? By road's the quickest. I'll get my car.'

The two men were gone. There had never been a chance for Cathleen to measure the significance of their first silence. Aunt Tilly's face, close to hers, looked thin and old and devouring.

'Speak up, girl. What did you find?'

'A dead man,' she said flatly.

It was Kitty, listening at the door, who fainted.

The postman was bicycling up the drive. Miss O'Riordan was telephoning the Galway police, Mary Kate was reviving Kitty, Patsy had taken Macushla to the stables. It was Cathleen who answered the boy's cheery greeting, and took the letters. The one on top was addressed to Miss Matilda O'Riordan in large untidy printing.

Cathleen had a small shock of surprise. She was almost certain it was the same printing as had been in the anonymous letter she had received.

She put the bundle of letters down on the table and went over to Kitty. She was, nevertheless, keenly aware of Miss O'Riordan putting down the telephone and coming back into the hall. It was the mail, not Kitty's fragile state of health, that instantly occupied her.

She pounced on the letters, then, with a curiously furtive movement, slid the top one into her pocket.

'Well, Kitty. That was a silly thing to do, wasn't it? You didn't find the body, as Mrs. Lamb did. I suppose you couldn't – ah – identify it, Mrs. Lamb?'

'I think so.' Cathleen was quite calm now. She was even able to watch Miss O'Riordan's deliberately casual expression with interest. The half-closed eyes were quite still, like a lizard's. 'There was the donkey, you see. So it must have been that tinker.'

'Lordy!' cried Mary Kate. 'The one who came to my kitchen door. Him with his cheeky grin and his blarney. I told Patsy, didn't I now, Patsy – ' her husband had come to the door to listen, ' – that he'd fall off his donkey drunk and break his neck. Didn't I now?'

'Is that how it was and all?' Patsy asked.

'He was in – that little blue lake.'

'Ho, and fallen in dead drunk then,' said Mary Kate triumphantly. 'We won't be wasting tears on the likes of him.'

Miss O'Riordan's shoulders had sagged the slightest bit. That was the only indication she showed of relief. In the deep pocket of her skirt Cathleen could see her fingers working at the letter, itching to tear it up. Rory must have told her yesterday of his suspicions about the tinker. If he had been blackmailing her, his death must be an exquisite relief.

But how was it that, drunk or otherwise, he had died so opportunely?

'The thunderstorm last night upset me,' Kitty was explaining weakly. 'And then hearing this—'

'One would almost think you'd tipped him in the lake,' her aunt said, with a return to her vigorous callousness. 'He's got his deserts, as Mary Kate says. Well, the police will be here shortly, and what does that do to our day's work, Mrs. Lamb? I suppose you'll say next you aren't fit to work.'

Her eyes were snapping with vitality. There was no doubt that she was enormously relieved. The man with the life gone from his bold dark face was no concern of hers as a man. Let his donkey, or whoever there was, grieve for him.

She was a selfish and insensitive woman, a bulldozer of a woman. And yet, last night in the dark, in her old-fashioned ball dress, she had been pathetic, a lost memory and nothing more.

But was this to be the end of it all? Cathleen wondered. Nothing had been solved about the child – if there were a child. Aunt Tilly's heirlooms were mysteriously saved, but that, so far, was all.

She kept thinking of Liam coming in so exhausted and dishevelled last night. And of Rory arriving unseen much later.

It was Rory who had been interested in finding the tinker.

But Liam hadn't been spending hours with a sick horse . . .

And anyway the man was a drunkard. She had seen that herself in Dublin. She had smelt liquor on his breath when he had thrust his head in the car. He must have stooped yesterday to scoop up water from the pool and fallen head first in, and then been too drunk to scramble out. He had probably been floating there at the time that she and Rory were asking for him in Loughneath.

Liam and Rory arrived back in a remarkably short time. While Liam, whose colour was better now although his eyes still had that look of deep shock, talked to Aunt Tilly, Rory asked Cathleen to come outside.

She went with him to the door. The bright morning had gone already, the woolly grey clouds had rolled up and there was a faint drizzle.

'I'm no doctor,' he said, 'but my guess is the fellow fell into the pool drunk.'

'That's what Mary Kate said.'

'He was poaching, anyway. We found snares. But listen. It'd be wise not to tell the police we were looking for him yesterday.'

'They'll tell that in Loughneath, anyway.'

'Oh, that's harmless enough. I'll say I suspected him of poaching. But the other. It's too fantastic a story and it's family business. I'd like you to say nothing.'

Cathleen searched his face. He wasn't distrait and shocked like Liam, he was basilisk like Aunt Tilly. He would pay a great deal for the family pride. It might suit his personal interests to pay.

She had thought she had begun to trust him. She wanted to weep.

He grasped her arm, hurting.

'My God, by the look on your face, you think I pushed him in that pool.'

'Where were you last night?' Cathleen heard the question asked before she could stop herself.

He threw up his head.

'Is it any business of yours?'

'Yes, it is, if you expect me to say nothing about the other. Why shouldn't the police start looking for a lost child?'

'The Galway police.' He gave a short bark of laughter. 'And a merry mess they'd make of it. A myth, a dream, a fairy tale. Police deal with facts. They don't even deal with circumstantial evidence such as torn letters and vague resemblances.'

There was the sound of a car coming down the drive. His grip on her arm was hurting her badly.

'Cathleen! This matters.'

'Oh, keep your secrets,' she said roughly. 'I'm tired of the lot of you. Melodramas, witchhunts.'

With that disconcerting change of demeanour, he gave her his irresistible smile, his eyes lighting, full of tenderness.

'Thank you, Cathleen. And in return, I was with Magdalene last night. We – talked, very late.'

He was a devil. He roused that flaming anger in her, and brought her back to the painful life she had wanted to avoid. Rory O'Riordan. Charmer, twister, bully, liar . . .

She was only someone to be kissed as a subterfuge . . .

CHAPTER THIRTEEN

THE tinker was known in Loughneath as Danny King. He had been drunk there the previous evening and had got into a fight. Finally he had stumbled off, shouting that one day he would drive up in a fine car and then they'd all pay him some respect. He had delusions that he was going to win the Irish Sweepstake, or some such easy money. It wasn't to be wondered at that he had met his death. He couldn't even sit astride his donkey, and the miracle was that he had got as far as the pool. He must have meant to camp there that night.

There was no doubt that it was death by misadventure, and no one too much the worse for it except Cathleen who had had the shock of finding the body.

She had obeyed Rory and said nothing to the heavy and solemn constable who questioned her, other than details of her shocking early morning discovery.

'What will happen about identification?' she asked the constable.

'That will be our headache, miss. These itinerant fellows are hard to track down. But if he has a family, we'll locate them eventually.'

So that was all. Except that Miss O'Riordan was in a sparkling and productive mood when they finally got down to work. She began to relate with great verve her brother Patrick's and one Captain Michael O'Neill's exploits in the rebellion.

'And there they were, taking their boots off and creeping in to sleep on the kitchen floor of the cottage while a Black and Tan, unsuspecting that the enemy was underneath, slept upstairs with his girl. And the owner of the cottage chuckling at the way she was getting her own back on the unwelcome lodger upstairs. The Irish love a good fight. I'm not past enjoying one myself. Anyone would be wise to think twice before threatening me.'

Her eyes glinted fiercely. She strode up and down, her step buoyant with relief. There was no doubt she did enjoy a fight with a visible enemy, but one whose weapons were telephone calls and threatening letters was another thing.

Cathleen suddenly had the feeling that it was not a child, but some other shameful secret Aunt Tilly was hiding. Liam, too, with his subterfuge of Red's illness, and Rory, solemnly taking her on that wild-goose chase after orphaned children. Even Kitty, fainting from shock, or revulsion, or simply relief.

Had the tinker known the secret they were hiding?

Liam came to her just before lunch. He looked himself again, well-groomed and smiling.

'Cathleen, darling, have you forgiven me again?'

'For what this time?'

'Jimmy tells me you were asking about Red. He was off colour, that's true, but not so bad that I couldn't leave him. Actually it was an important family reason—'

'Which isn't my business.'

He smiled, gently and beguilingly. These O'Riordan men knew how to flash on charm like a rainbow.

'It would only bore you. Forget it, will you, please? What do you think, Aunt Tilly, the old sport, has promised to put up Red's fees for the Grand National. I'm going to start training him right away.'

'Yourself?'

'I could take that horse over a haystack. He jumps like a bird flying. He'll make me my fortune, you'll see.'

'Well, good luck,' said Cathleen uneasily. Liam's eyes were the deep burning blue of water beneath bright sunshine, the blue of the Connemara lakes. It was a mistake to think him quiet and philosophic. He had more than his share of the O'Riordan's fighting fanatical spirit. And presumably the money which Aunt Tilly wouldn't now be requiring for an irritating blackmailer was to be devoted to the furthering of the grand sport of horse racing.

'Do you forgive me, Cathleen?'

She shrugged. 'It seems, if I stay here, I'll spend my time forgiving you unpredictable Irish.'

'Bless you, Cathleen. But let's keep it in the singular. More deserving, do you follow me?'

She understood well enough. She wasn't either to trust or forgive Rory if he asked her to. Not that he was likely to ask. He would never feel in the need of forgiveness. What he did, he did, and that was that.

She also knew better than to press Liam for an explanation as to why Rory had asked him to stay home while he himself went to Dublin. The O'Riordans stood together.

But there was one thing she was determined to ask.

'You didn't catch a cold from your wetting last night?'

'Good lord, no. How soft do you think I am?'

'Not as subject to chills as your horse?'

'Oh, all right, clever puss. I was in Loughneath at a poker school. We have a room at the hotel. I don't broadcast this. Aunt Tilly thinks she's the only one in this family entitled to gamble.'

'Then you must have seen the fight the tinker got into.'

'No, I didn't. That happened before I arrived. I heard about it.'

'You did get wet,' Cathleen murmured. 'Why didn't you take your car?'

'Jesus, Mary and Joseph!' he exclaimed admiringly. 'You'd make a prosecuting counsel. Why didn't I take my car, she says. I did. But as you know, it's an old car. It doesn't much care for heavy rain. It stopped just inside the gates. I had to walk all the way up the drive. It's still there.

I've got a man coming out from Loughneath to look at it. And now, flattering as it is to be asked questions by you, will you stop it, and come and have a drink.'

Aunt Tilly found them sipping sherry, but instead of giving her fearful scowl, she said affably, 'I'll join you. My usual, Liam. And this afternoon I want you to go into Galway to pick up the supplies I've ordered for the orphans. If your car's out of action, you'll have to take the Rolls. Now isn't it God's mercy that wretched man wasn't found while the orphans were here.'

Peggy Moloney came bicycling back from her afternoon off in a state of excitement. She met Cathleen on the stairs, and looking round quickly to see if anyone was listening, said.

'What do you think! That Eileen Burke has disappeared.'

'Disappeared!' It was the cool of the banister beneath her hand that made her feel cool all over. 'You mean she's left Loughneath?'

'She has and all, and not a word to anybody. It just looks, my Mam says, as if she'd done a midnight flit.'

'The baby's gone, too?' Cathleen asked, pursuing her first instinctive thought.

'Well, of course,' said Peggy. 'She wouldn't be leaving a young child, now would she?'

She would if – Cathleen cut the thought off in her mind. She might have nightmares about that face like a frog's underbelly floating in the water, but she wouldn't have them while wide awake in the daytime. Because Eileen Burke had left Loughneath, it didn't mean that she was dead.

'Mrs. Murphy in the hotel next door, said the baby was crying a lot in the night. Then it stopped and she dropped off to sleep, and didn't hear anything more. It wasn't until the milk wasn't taken in that she thought she ought to investigate. The door wasn't locked and the house was empty.'

'Perhaps her husband had come for her,' Cathleen said, without conviction.

'More likely she's gone off with a man. That's what everyone's saying. She was a fast piece, and Mam says she'll get what's coming to her. All those beads and bangles and all. It shows the type. But it is a shame about the little boy. Did you ever see him, Mrs. Lamb? He was a bonny little fellow.'

'People would have heard a car stopping,' Cathleen said.

'It was raining so hard most of the night, you wouldn't hear much else. She might have gone by the bus early this morning. Mam says it's none of our business. The woman had no obligations to anyone except Mrs. Murphy for the house, and there wasn't more than a day's rent owing. Do you know, she didn't once go to Mass. You'd have thought she'd want to say a prayer for her husband away in a foreign country, wouldn't you now?'

Kitty wasn't well that evening. She came to Cathleen's room just before dinner and asked if Cathleen would apologize to Aunt Tilly for her. She had one of her migraines, she said.

She did look flushed and strained. Her eyes were enormous, and full of some obscure fear. Cathleen thought that her attack of hysteria during the storm combined with the shock of the drowned tinker this morning had been too much for her.

'Of course I'll tell your aunt,' she said sympathetically. 'Have you taken some aspirin?'

Kitty nodded.

'Then why don't you go to bed and I'll see if Mary Kate can bring up a tray, or I'll bring one myself.'

'No, I couldn't eat anything, thank you. Though it's kind of you.'

The poor little thing was feeling too tired and nervous to face her aunt. Which one could well understand, for the thought of that forbidding figure at one's bedside would shock one into illness. Cathleen was touched that she had come to her, and responded to her appeal.

'I'll come in and see you later. And if you're scared—'

'Scared!'

'I only meant it looks thundery again. Do call me if you want me.'

Kitty's eyes brimmed with sudden tears. She seemed about to say something, then changed her mind and went away.

But later, when Cathleen went to see how she was, her room was empty. Nor was she with her mother. Cathleen meant to stay only a moment up there, but Peggy Moloney beckoned to her and whispered.

'I really think she tried to say words this evening. She made quite a different sound. It was like "Lie, Lie, Lie!" '

'Perhaps she wanted Liam.'

'Why, yes, I never thought of that. I thought she was having some nightmare, poor little thing.'

The small crumpled face stared up from the snowy pillow, unseeing, unhearing. Cathleen patted the quiet hands, and smiled encouragingly.

'You're better tonight, Mrs. O'Riordan?'

There was no flicker of expression in the milky wide-open eyes.

Cathleen moved away from the bedside.

'Has Kitty been up this evening?'

'I've not seen a sign of her.'

'She wasn't feeling well. She must have gone out for some air.'

This proved to be so, for as Cathleen went down she met Kitty hurrying up the stairs. The colour was even brighter in her cheeks, and she gasped, 'Was my aunt annoyed with me for not coming down to dinner?'

'She was only worried that you might not be well for tomorrow. You do look better. Have you been out in the garden?'

'Yes. Until it got dark. The fresh air did my head good.'

'That's fine. I'd go to bed now, if I were you, since it looks as if none of us will be spared tomorrow.'

'Those horrible children!' Kitty exclaimed. Then she added quickly, 'I didn't mean that. Only I have this every year, and it's no joke.'

'I don't suppose it is. But I'll help. I'm not allergic to small children.'

Kitty gave her a quick glance.

'Neither am I when I have the energy, but I just don't know how—' She stopped as if she had been afraid of saying too much. 'I'm going to bed, Mrs. Lamb. Good-night.'

Cathleen went to bed early, too, but nobody else did. Very late she heard Miss O'Riordan coming up the stairs laughing uproariously. She called to somebody.

'Not a second late for breakfast, mind! After tomorrow we can rest on our laurels. Heigh ho, what a relief that will be!'

It had been a long day, but for Miss O'Riordan and one of her nephews, or perhaps both of them, a festive night. It seemed as if it would be only Cathleen and perhaps the over-sensitive Kitty who had nightmares about a tinker, dead by accident.

She had no idea what time Liam and Rory went to bed, for she fell asleep herself and woke only once. That was when she thought she saw a tiny flicker of light in one of the windows of the west wing. It was so small and pale it could have been a candle flame. But it must have been only the reflection of the sinking moon, for the west wing was closed. No one ever went there.

Patsy was out early in the morning, tidying the gravel

paths. Cathleen heard the scrape of his rake beneath her window, and leaned out to call good morning to him.

He lifted his disgruntled face.

'Traipsing, traipsing, traipsing,' he said. 'That'll be the way of it all day. I don't know why I bother to tidy up now. Postman's been, miss. Letter for you.'

The cool finger of apprehension touched her again. A letter for her. The only letter she had had here had been the anonymous one.

She flew downstairs to find two letters on the hall table. The top one was for herself, and with relief she saw that it was from Ronald Gault, who no doubt wondered how she was getting on, and why he hadn't heard from her. It was the one underneath that made her stand still, her scalp prickling.

It was addressed to Miss Matilda O'Riordan, and it was written in that now familiar laborious printing. The postmark, Cathleen noticed, was Galway. The letter had been posted at eleven o'clock the previous evening. Approximately twenty-four hours after the death of the tinker . . .

'Ah, I'm glad to see you up and about, Mrs. Lamb,' came Miss O'Riordan's vigorous voice. 'I might be asking you as a favour to help Mary Kate in the kitchen today. You said you didn't mind what you did. Some mail? Bills, I expect.'

Cathleen handed her the letter, watching her face. It registered plain astonishment. Her shock was such that she even forgot Cathleen's presence and with tense fingers ripped open the envelope.

'What is it, Miss O'Riordan?'

She started, looking at Cathleen with an absent air. Her face seemed to have grown much older. Then she recollected herself and pushed the paper and envelope into her pocket.

'Nothing,' she said. Her eyes became hostile. 'Why do you ask?'

'I thought you looked upset.'

'I don't enjoy begging letters, if you must know. I see no reason why you should know. Where are my nephews? Where's Kitty? Why isn't anyone down? I told them not to be late.'

'Miss O'Riordan, is someone threatening you?' Cathleen's anxiety made her speak.

She was rewarded with a ferocious stare.

'Threatening *me*! Who would dare?'

She strode away. It was Cathleen who was trembling, not from fear but pure shock. The tinker wasn't dead. Her dreadful discovery had all been imagination. Or if he were, he had been innocent, a merely annoying and persistent purveyor of his wares. Someone else, someone unknown, was the persecutor.

The day bade fair to be a disaster. Kitty, very pale and looking as if she hadn't slept at all, came down to be at once the butt for her aunt's temper.

'How can you look like that, today of all days? Washed out, feeble, not fit to be seen!'

'I'm sorry, Aunt Tilly. My head isn't better yet.'

'Then have some coffee and take some more aspirin. No, don't take aspirin, I'll dose you up with some good Irish whisky. My God, where are those lazy boys? They'll have to be leaving for the station shortly.'

'Here I am, Aunt Tilly,' said Liam, strolling in, dressed in riding clothes. 'I've been exercising the horses. You should have come out with me, Cathleen. Post been?'

'It has,' said Aunt Tilly. 'I don't know why you ask. It never brings anything but trouble.'

'Trouble?'

'Bills, begging letters. Give, give, give! What do they think we are? The Bank of Ireland? Well, thanks be, here's Rory at last. Now we can get breakfast over.'

'Who's treating you like the bank?' Rory asked.

'Everyone!' said Aunt Tilly. 'Everyone! As well you know.'

'But I don't know, Aunt Tilly. Who?'

'Leave it be!' Aunt Tilly screamed. 'I make an idle remark, and there's all this fuss. Now can we get this dreadful day organized? And thankful I'll be when I can close my eyes this evening.'

The woman was a superb actress. For when the two meek sisters in their black habits arrived with the gaggle of small children, Aunt Tilly's manner showed nothing but graciousness. One would have thought she had waited all the year for the pleasure of this day and her contribution towards the less fortunate. In her black dress, she swooped about like a long-legged crane, scaring the little ones into speechlessness and organizing the adults, including the glowering Mary Kate and Patsy, with firm authority.

It had been arranged that Cathleen and Kitty supervise the children's lunch in the dining-room while Miss O'Riordan took care of Sister Mary Martha and Sister Veronica in the library. The sisters were to rest, the children were to make as much noise as they cared to.

But on the whole they were an awestruck and timid collection. They were too young and the day was being too much for them. The possessor of the most vitality was the square and belligerent redhead, Peter Brady. Cathleen couldn't take her eyes off him. She pondered, as Rory must have done, the boy's true identity. He was an engaging youngster with a wide grin and fearless eyes.

Cathleen tried to ask him questions.

'Do you like being in the orphanage, Peter?'

'It's foine.'

'Have you been there long?'

'I have.' He darted off into a wild game, plunging over Patsy's neatly dug beds. When Cathleen had captured him again he was giggling wildly and out of breath.

'Peter, where's your mother?'

He stared at her comprehendingly.

'Where's your Mammy?'

'One day I went away.'

'From where, Peter? From who?'

'I sleeps in a dormtry. We all sleeps in dormtries.' He wriggled free. 'I want to play.'

'Peter, have you got a father?'

The bright blue eyes beneath the shock of red hair stared at her impatiently.

'I want to play, I want to play.'

He was too little. He had already forgotten where he had come from. The stocky little body, the engaging, impudent face had all the virility of the O'Riordans. But there was no physical resemblance.

Later she realized Rory was standing beside her. He looked thoughtful, perhaps slightly amused. It wasn't easy to read his expression. But he, too, was watching Peter Brady.

'He deserves better than a drunkard for a father, doesn't he?'

'He's too little to talk sense,' Cathleen burst out.

Rory began to laugh. 'That must be frustrating for you.' He gave her his insolent assessing gaze. 'Are you still determined to solve our problems? You won't, you know. One simply produces another.'

This was so true that Cathleen was provoked into exclaiming, 'Rory, your aunt's still being blackmailed!'

'Who by? All these little boys?'

'Rory, for heaven's sake! Something dreadful will happen. I'm sure it will. You should have seen her this morning. She was terrified.'

'Aunt Tilly terrified! Never!' He was still laughing softly, but his eyes were thoughtful and quite cold.

The day ended with Patsy losing his temper, and doing a dance of rage, a comic little figure shaking his fists at a collection of suddenly awed and silent children.

'Oh, the divil fly wi' ye all, and good riddance! I niver seen the likes since Mr. Rory and Mr. Shamus were little lads. Git away wi' ye all!'

He lunged at them and the children scattered in all directions.

'Shame on you, Patsy!' called Mary Kate. 'And the day just over.'

'Niver soon enough for me!'

The cars were at the door, Rory's shabby roadster and the Rolls. One of the children was missing. Peter Brady. Miss O'Riordan, too, was missing. She was in the library, the red-headed boy half asleep on her lap. His shock of bright hair, his drowsy face, was pressed against her flat bosom.

She sprang up, roughly shaking him, when Cathleen came in.

'Everyone's ready to go, Miss O'Riordan.'

'We're coming, we're coming. This child hadn't a word to say to me until he needed a place to put his head. Don't ever let anyone convince you that children are innocent. They'll use you every time.'

The children piled into the cars, disappearing magically into the depths. The two sisters, wrapping their habits round themselves like bats' wings, followed, one in each car. Liam and Rory took the wheels. Aunt Tilly, no shred of her graciousness lost, waved and smiled. Kitty, paler than ever, stood behind her, obviously longing for nothing but to escape to her room. Cathleen searched for the red-headed Peter Brady. But now the cars were too far away. She couldn't see him.

'Thank heaven!' said Aunt Tilly, sinking into the nearest chair. 'Kitty, don't be saying what's in your eyes. Sure, I'm a hypocrite. But one with a sense of humour, I trust. Mrs. Lamb, could you possibly find the energy to fetch a bottle of whisky and glasses. In a moment I've got to face Patsy. I suspect he has a wicked look to him. The stony-hearted old divil, not to have more sympathy for mere babies. Though I confess I found the whole batch of them remarkably uninteresting. Except perhaps the little fellow I personally sponsored. He lived in a slum with dreadful parents. It was a pleasure to see him looking so well. He looked like a child who'd make his way in the world, given a chance.'

But it seemed as if that might be the last glimpse Miss O'Riordan would have of the child who just possibly might have been her own nephew. For that evening there was frantic telephoning from Dublin.

It was Sister Mary Martha crying incoherently that somewhere between Loughneath Castle and Dublin Peter Brady had disappeared.

CHAPTER FOURTEEN

'WHICH one was Peter Brady?' Liam wanted to know.

'The redhead.'

'They all looked alike to me.'

'They couldn't have!' Aunt Tilly said angrily. 'Haven't you eyes? The redhead was the only one with any personality. Which of you had him in your car? I brought him out at the last minute, but I didn't see which car he got into.'

Rory swore he hadn't been in his. Liam refused to be interested.

'I told you, I didn't pick one from another. What does it matter if he's jumped off the train?'

'Liam!' Aunt Tilly was sitting upright, her eyes sparking fiercely. 'A three-year-old doesn't jump off a train. But if he's fallen off, he may be killed. For heaven's sake, take the thing seriously.'

'By all means, Aunt Tilly. What would you like me to do? Drive alongside the railway line for a hundred miles?'

'You fool!' said Aunt Tilly, in a low deadly voice. 'Don't you realize this child must be found.' She sprang up. 'You're taking me to Dublin.'

'Now?'

'Now.'

Kitty gave a stifled gasp. Rory sprang up.

'I'll take you, Aunt Tilly.'

Cathleen had the queer feeling that Liam, who had been joking, hadn't been joking at all. He said slowly, 'What a bore. I told you this day would be a disaster. Then go and get yourself ready, Aunt Tilly. Don't worry, Rory. I'll take her.'

'Isn't your car out of action?'

'No. Joe O'Gorman came up and fixed it.'

It was a battle of wills. For all his assumed reluctance, Liam was as anxious to go as Rory. They both had a reason to be desperately interested in the disappearance of small Peter Brady. Cathleen watched with detached interest, wondering which one would win. It didn't much matter, because if Liam won, Rory would follow. Or more likely get to Dublin first. She knew him well enough for that.

But what was it all about?

In almost no time the suspense was over. The telephone rang again. Aunt Tilly grabbed it and listened, her long face growing deeply perplexed.

'You're sure this is true, Sister? Yes. Yes, I agree. Why should he bother to ring you otherwise? Ah, yes, it's a great pity. Yes, yes, yes . . .' Her voice was growing more impatient. 'Then we'll discuss it again in the morning, Sister. Ah, yes, you can be sure . . .'

She slammed down the receiver. She was breathing quickly. She was looking as she had done that morning when the letter had come, pinched and driven.

'Would you believe it, the child's father snatched the boy off the Dublin railway station when the train came in and took him home. Said he'd changed his mind about the boy having a good life. The selfish beast. Taking the little one back to that squalor. Giving us all a fine fright. What's to be done now?'

'If this man is really the boy's father,' said Rory, 'nothing can be done. The point is –' he looked from one to the other, ' – can he prove it?'

Liam looked at his aunt.

'You're in the best position to know that, Aunt Tilly. Didn't you interview the man?'

'Who said I did? I was led to believe the child had been

abandoned.' Aunt Tilly's nostrils were twitching. 'I've been treated like a fool. I won't allow the matter to rest.'

Liam put his arm round her.

'You're getting yourself into a state. Sleep on it. Talk about it in the morning.'

'Sleep!' She suddenly realized she had whispered the word in incredulity, and began belatedly to laugh at herself. For a moment her histrionic ability had deserted her. 'Yes, you're right, Liam. I'm getting the matter out of proportion. Would you have thought, Mrs. Lamb, I cared so much about my orphans? You thought me a heartless woman, didn't you? And here I am, showing you a heart as soft as butter. And what's wrong with you, miss?'

She swung round on Kitty who, inexplicably, had begun to giggle.

'N-nothing, Aunt Tilly. It's j-just—' Her explanation was lost in giggles that grew more and more uncontrollable. She was almost in hysterics. It was only when Liam said, 'Here, steady on,' that by a terrific effort she controlled herself. 'I'm sorry,' she said weakly. 'It's not that I think it funny. I guess I'm – just tired.'

'So are we all,' said Aunt Tilly. 'I propose an early night.'

And that night Cathleen heard the baby crying.

She turned over and buried her head in the pillow. There wasn't a baby. It was Mrs. O'Riordan upstairs. Or an owl, or some other nightbird. Or the wind down the chimney. Or simply a sound in her own head, a memory of Debby that struck her most when her defences were weak with sleep.

She succeeded in convincing herself that one of these theories, or all of them, were true, and was drowsing back into sleep when the sound came again, much more clearly. It was quite definitely someone crying. There was an edge of distress to the sobs that required investigation.

It must be Mrs. O'Riordan. Peggy must have fallen asleep too soundly. She was little more than a child, and needed her sleep. Cathleen sprang out of bed. She had better go up and see.

The night-light burnt dimly beside Mrs. O'Riordan's bed. The patient lay very quietly, her eyes shut. Apart from her gentle breathing, one might have thought she had died. She was certainly much too deeply asleep to have been crying so recently.

Peggy, who was a light sleeper after all, emerged from her bed in the adjoining room.

'Oh, it's you!' she whispered. 'I thought I heard someone. What's the matter? She didn't call out, did she?'

'I thought she was crying.'

'I didn't hear anything. I always do hear.' Peggy looked at her patient. 'She hasn't stirred for hours, by the look of her. And she isn't likely to, because I increased her sleeping dose tonight. The doctor said I should if she was restless.'

'Was she restless?'

'She seemed so. I don't know if she heard the children during the day. They were shouting and screaming under the window once or twice. You know, a child might be able to rouse her more than a grown-up. If she's living in the past, she might be thinking of her own babies.'

'It was a baby I thought I heard tonight,' Cathleen confessed. 'I suppose you could say I was living in the past, too. I'm sorry I disturbed you, Peggy.'

'That's all right,' said Peggy cheerfully. 'Why don't you take a sleeping tablet if you're having nightmares. It's not to be wondered at, after the day you've had. I'll give you one of my patient's. Now that's funny.' She was looking on the table where the medicine bottles and tumblers were neatly arranged. 'The bottle's not here. Where could I have put it?'

She switched on the flashlight which she carried in her pocket, and looked more closely.

'Oh, here it is. Now isn't that funny. I always put it back in exactly the same place, but it's right at the other end of the table. I must have been absent-minded.'

'Or someone else moved it,' Cathleen suggested, watching Peggy shake out a pink tablet.

'Maybe,' said Peggy. 'Though I don't know why. You take that, Mrs. Lamb, and you'll be asleep in five minutes.'

There was no sound of crying any more. Cathleen went softly back to her room convinced now that she had imagined the whole thing. She swallowed the tablet Peggy had given her, and got back into bed. It was bliss to relax, to push every thought out of her mind, and let drowsiness overtake her. She would probably sleep in in the morning, and miss the ride she had planned with Liam. She had wanted to watch him schooling Red in the lower field where he had set up hurdles. But there would be plenty more opportunities. She would be here until the end of the summer at least, when the leaves began to fall, and the smoky mists rolled up, and fires were lit in the enormous fireplaces, and Miss O'Riordan wore her sable cape during the day as well as the night, and Rory could no longer spend sixteen hours a day outdoors . . .

And the baby would be three months older . . . She was almost asleep and dreaming. It was the nursery rhyme ringing in her head that brought that odd thought. It had been one of Debby's favourites.

Hey diddle diddle, the cat and the fiddle . . .

The words were not in her head at all. They were being sung by someone in a clear far-away voice.

Cathleen shot up on the pillows, her ears strained to listen. But now her head was woolly with sleep. Why ever had she taken that pill? She had known she must be on the alert day and night. Day and night . . .

She couldn't hear a thing except the intermittent rustle of ivy leaves against the wall. There were little flurries of wind. It was the wind that, for a few paralysed moments, sounded like soft footsteps.

A door closed somewhere. Or did it? Cathleen opened her eyes to find she had fallen sound asleep sitting half upright, her head fallen sideways on the pillow. Sunlight was streaming in the window, and there were horses' hooves crunching on the gravel beneath her window.

'Cathleen! You lazy hound! Why didn't you get up and come for a ride?'

The night, with its half-dreams and alarms, was over. She grabbed her wrap and ran to the window.

'I'm sorry, Liam. I overslept.'

'And it's a wonderful morning. Red's been jumping like a dream.'

Pleasure at his horse's performance made Liam look excited and vigorous and alert.

'Come on down, Rapunzel.'

Cathleen realized that her hair was streaming on her shoulders.

'I must look like a witch.'

'A witch it is,' agreed Liam, grinning. But in one of her irritating switches of thought, it was Rory's voice in her head. 'I like you with your hair down.' The brothers had similar tastes. They both flirted, and then went their secret ways . . .

Cathleen drew back, the day suddenly pressing on her. Had the postman been? What sort of a mood would Miss O'Riordan be in? Was Kitty's head better? Above all, what would this day hold in the way of alarms and mysteries?

Although she was late for breakfast, she paused to knock at Kitty's door to see if she were up and feeling better. When there was no answer she pushed the door gently and looked into the room.

It was very tidy. Although it was so early in the day the bed was made. It almost looked as if it hadn't been slept in.

Instantly, the obscure alarm was beating in Cathleen's throat again. She hurried downstairs and was inordinately relieved to see Kitty sitting at the breakfast table. She had, for one moment, been thinking of that sharp-eyed secretive woman, Eileen Burke, and her silent departure. That sleeping pill must have left her in a daze where she was unable to distinguish reality from imagination.

She apologized for being late, and added, 'I hope your head is better, Kitty. I looked in to see if you were up.'

Kitty's eyes flicked up and down.

'I got up early and made my bed and went into the garden. It's the best time of day.'

Aunt Tilly looked at her keenly.

'It's not often you've realized that. You must be feeling spry this morning.'

'I went to bed so early,' Kitty murmured. She flushed, self-conscious with everyone's eyes on her. 'Anyway, I feel fine today.'

But when her flush died she didn't look fine at all. There were shadows of tiredness round her eyes. She looked washed out.

It was the beginning of an uneasy day. Immediately after breakfast Rory got in his car and went off somewhere, speeding down the drive as if he were in a great hurry. Cathleen saw Liam watching him go, with speculation in his eyes. Aunt Tilly disappeared upstairs, and didn't come down to the library where Cathleen was working until just before lunch.

'Sorry,' she said briefly. 'I have distractions today.'

'Are you worried about something, Miss O'Riordan?'

'Use your head, Mrs. Lamb! I'm always worried. Wouldn't you be, running a castle. Such as it is, with dry rot, and carpets falling to pieces, and no servants, and my sister-in-law taking forever to die, and nurses costing money, and this wanted, that wanted, everything wanted. There's never an end to it. There's never going to be.' She paused a moment, as if her own words frightened her.

'It would be better if Rory or Liam married,' Cathleen took the opportunity of saying. 'Then his wife could take a great deal of the burden off your shoulders.'

Miss O'Riordan stopped in her stride. She gave Cathleen a narrowed, indescribably leering look.

'Now bigamy would be the last thing this family needs!'

The blood beat in Cathleen's temples.

'I don't know what you're suggesting, Miss O'Riordan.'

'No? Well, leave it alone. It's not part of your work!'

'I thought I heard a baby crying in the night,' Cathleen said in a rush.

She was given a long, keen suspicious stare. Then, 'Impossible!' said Miss O'Riordan, and walked out, leaving Cathleen in a state of deep confusion and worry. Bigamy? That was a new thought.

Later Cathleen found Miss O'Riordan standing staring speculatively at the painting of the gipsy.

'What a pity it's not a Romney,' she was saying to herself. She was obviously taking stock of her assets. She would have no qualms about selling something that was a family heirloom, whether the money was meant for the purchase of new carpets, or – what else?

She gave her shoulders a shake. She looked old and tired, a thin dried-up tree that might break in the next gale. And what was the use of her realizing sums of money if Rory took them away from her . . .

In the late dusk Cathleen strolled in the garden. Again, neither Liam nor Rory had been in to dinner. No remark was made about their absence, but Miss O'Riordan was more testy than ever, crumbling her bread, and eating little. Kitty had the feverish colour back in her cheeks. She seemed to be listening all the time. For Liam's return, probably. She was always happier when he was there.

There had been no telephone calls and no strange letters. That was the only relief there had been all the long difficult day.

But now it was pleasant to walk across Patsy's well-mowed lawns and smell the stocks and tobacco plants and feel the damp air, soft with incipient rain, on her face. For a very brief time Cathleen had a sense of well-being and content, almost an anticipation of happiness. Then abruptly it was lost.

She had happened to glance up to see whose lights were on. Mrs. O'Riordan's, Kitty's, Aunt Tilly's? And saw instead the flicker of light in the west wing.

It was as if someone had carried a lighted lamp or a candle past the middle window, and into another room not visible from here.

Cathleen flew to the kitchen.

'Come out here,' she said breathlessly to Mary Kate, who was clattering dishes at the sink. 'I want you to look.'

Mary Kate dropped the dish cloth in a hurry. Her rosy face was full of alarm.

'What is it now?' she cried, as if alarms were things to be expected at Loughneath Castle.

'There's a light in the west wing. Oh no, it's gone now I saw it just a moment ago.'

'A light? But the place is empty.'

Patsy had come to join them. He screwed up his eyes and looked up at the long dark windows.

'I'm thinking you must have been seeing a ghost.'

'But it was a light,' Cathleen insisted. 'I thought I saw one in the night, too.'

'Ah, now, you must have been dreaming, miss. Or it could be the moon. Look, there you are now. The moon's just rising. You see how it shines in the windows.'

It was true that the moon, an enormous saffron-coloured one, had just floated clear of the trees, and now there was a frail nebulous shine to all the windows of the west wing. But five minutes ago the moon hadn't been clear. And the light had been in only one window, flitting by, a ghost-light as Patsy had said.

Cathleen clasped her arms round herself. The night was so warm and soft, but she was shivering.

'The door to the west wing is locked,' Mary Kate was saying. 'The rooms up there haven't been used since the master died, God rest him. I go up once in twelve months, maybe, and take a look about. There's nothing there but old furniture. Even all the best carpets were taken up to use in this part of the castle. There might be bats, or a bird fallen down a chimney. That's all. Sure, and you're seeing things, miss. And no wonder, all that book work you're doing. You're living with ghosts, you might say.'

'I heard a baby crying,' Cathleen said under her breath.

Mary Kate shot her a sharp glance.

'Sure, and I do, too, sometimes. The little one Patsy and I never had.'

Patsy made an impatient sound and turned and stumped off, a bandy-legged little fellow more than ever like a leprechaun in this haunted dusk.

'He can't stand sentimental women,' Mary Kate said. 'It's never the pain to a man 'tis to a woman not to have a child. Then come on in, my dear. The dusk isn't good for fancies.'

Cathleen went in willingly enough, but she wasn't satisfied. As soon as Mary Kate was busy with the dishes again she intended to do a little exploring. She should have done it earlier today. Now it was just light enough to manage without candles or an electric torch. She would try to go quietly. She imagined she would only find Miss O'Riordan, perhaps dressed in one of her gowns from the nostalgic past, wandering about rooms haunted only with her particular ghosts. But at least she must find something. For she knew there had been that fleeting and furtive light that did not come from any moon.

Mary Kate had said the door leading to the west wing was locked. That was the first thing that set Cathleen's heart beating madly. For it was unlocked, and slid open easily at her touch. She found herself in a hall with a cavernous fireplace, coal-black in the dusk. At the opposite end was a staircase leading up into darkness almost as black as that in which the fireplace was swallowed. She had to grope her way, the faint gritty feel of dust on the uncovered boards beneath her feet.

She was beginning to think that it was too dark and that she should have brought a light. But at the top of the staircase the last daylight fell through a long window (the window that had momentarily encased that other flickering light?) and it was possible to see the long passage and the closed doors on either side. The floor and the walls were bare.

No, not quite bare. A small object lay near the top of the stairs. It looked like a mouse. Cathleen touched it tentatively with her foot. Then she gasped, and picked it up. It surely couldn't be— She turned to what little light there was from the staircase window, holding up the object.

She was so startled and absorbed with her discovery that she didn't hear a sound until the heavy object was flung against her. There wasn't a chance to preserve her balance. In the instant of falling she knew that some person had hurtled out of one of the rooms immediately behind her. With her last conscious instinct, she clutched in her hand the baby's shoe.

CHAPTER FIFTEEN

CATHLEEN could see nothing but the tall shape, rigid as a post, beside her.

What was it – a scarecrow dressed in a shabby tweed suit, its hair slightly awry in the wind. A poker-backed scarecrow towering over her as she lay in the field. No, not a field. A bed. She could feel the bedclothes over her legs which seemed to be aching badly. Or was it her head that ached?

Beyond the scarecrow seemed to be fields of flowers, fading in the hot sun. Cathleen blinked her eyes, trying desperately to focus, to come out of this nightmare that was holding her so painfully.

The flowers were on the wall. They were the chrysanthemums and lanterns painted on the faded Chinese wallpaper. She had admired them once, thinking it a pity they were now shabby and colourless. It must have been an expensive wallpaper a long time ago, she had thought, when these people were rich.

What people?

She made a tremendous effort and raised her head. The pain made her gasp. The scarecrow turned, and the long white, menacing familiar face hung over hers.

'Well,' said Aunt Tilly, without emotion. 'How are you feeling now?'

'Terrible,' said Cathleen. 'I must be ill.'

She was full of despair that she should be ill and a trouble to Miss O'Riordan. How could it have happened? She didn't remember going to bed . . .

'The doctor said you would have a bad headache for a time. It's nothing to worry about. You're very lucky.'

The severe, emotionless voice made the pain in her head stab violently. How could she possibly be lucky, lying here suffering?

'I'm sorry.' She was beginning to remember. 'It will hold up our work.'

She wasn't being paid to lie in bed gazing at expensive wallpaper, or looking at the view, misty blue and green as a dream, through the long window. Neither did she want overworked Mary Kate or Kitty grudgingly waiting on her, and least of all Miss O'Riordan, like a wardress, sitting at her bedside.

'You should have thought of that before you indulged your impertinent curiosity and went snooping all over the house without asking anyone's permission.'

'Snooping!' echoed Cathleen, with weak indignation.

'How else were you found unconscious at the foot of the stairs in an unused part of the house? It was only by chance I saw the door open.'

The dark staircase, the empty rooms, the will o' the wisp light, the violently colliding body . . .

'The baby's shoe!' gasped Cathleen, and the pain stabbed unbearably through her head, sending the long intent face above her into welcome mist . . .

She didn't know how long Miss O'Riordan had been saying in that harsh rasping voice,

'What shoe? What are you talking about?'

Cathleen's fingers curved over the empty palm.

'There was one on the stairs. I picked it up.'

'Nonsense! I'm afraid your fall has affected your head. There was nothing whatever in your hands when I found you. I'd have noticed it immediately.'

Miss O'Riordan's face came nearer. Cathleen narrowed her eyes, trying to see more clearly. There was a faint shine of perspiration on the bony brow. Why? Was it such a hot day? What day was it?

'You poor child, you've been thinking of your own baby. You've allowed that tragedy to affect your mind. You must rest.'

'How can I?'

She had thought it was a mouse. She had only just picked it up, before she fell, noticing that it was pale blue and with a lace hanging out, the kind of shoe meant to be tied firmly on to a toddler who would be tempted to scuff it off. It was exactly the kind of shoe and the size that Debby had been wearing ...

Had she imagined it?

But she remembered so clearly picking it up before she fell.

Someone must have taken it out of her hand before calling for help.

Miss O'Riordan had found her ...

Cathleen sank deeper into the pillow, trying to inch away from the face bending hypnotically over her.

'What time is it?'

'It's almost lunch-time. You've slept for nearly eighteen hours. The doctor said you would. He also said you might be a little confused for some time. You've had slight concussion, and I dare say plenty of bruises.' She straightened herself. She looked eight feet tall, a gangling scarecrow made out of an outsize broomstick. 'Now don't be alarmed. I'm not going to leave you. I'm merely going to call Kitty to bring you some hot soup.'

'I'd like to be alone,' Cathleen said as strongly as she could manage. But Miss O'Riordan was at the door, and didn't hear, or affected not to. After speaking to Kitty who must have been somewhere very close at hand, she came back and took her place at the bedside once more.

She wasn't a scarecrow after all, she was one of the fighting harsh-voiced crows all insistent on getting their place on the overloaded branch of that poor crooked tree. She was the strongest, the tallest, the bossiest of them all. It would be no use to try to push her away, to disagree with her. What she said and did must be right.

'Come along. Open your mouth, Mrs. Lamb.'

Somehow the soup was there, steaming and savoury. It was simplest to obey and swallow a few mouthfuls. It was also wise, for the nourishment cleared her vision a little, and presently she saw that Kitty stood beyond Miss O'Riordan watching. Kitty's face was paper white, her eyes as enormous and empty as her mother's.

'There,' said Miss O'Riordan. 'Now you must sleep again. I'll stay beside you. Kitty, take the tray away.'

'If you want to rest, Aunt Tilly—'

'I don't want to rest.'

'But you've been up all night.'

'I dozed in my chair. I may do so again.'

'Very well, Aunt Tilly.'

But she never let sleep overcome her, Cathleen thought, she sat upright, her eyes unblinking, her long nose pointed at the ceiling forever.

If only she would go away. Now that she could think a little more clearly Cathleen realized that Miss O'Riordan must be afraid Cathleen would murmur something in her sleep, something someone else may hear and misinterpret. A silly story about finding a baby's shoe . . .

Do you think we shut it in an empty room and starve it . . .

The remembered fragment of conversation set Cathleen's heart thumping. Then the thumping extended to her head and a pendulum beat painfully against her temples. She had to close her eyes in protest . . .

And the whistle came out of the darkness, the sweet liquid sound . . .

> There's a colleen fair as may,
> For a year and for a day . . .

Cathleen started up wildly in the hot bed.

'The tinker!' she cried. 'The tinker's back!'

The room was almost dark. Miss O'Riordan's shape was a thin shadow.

'What tinker, Mrs. Lamb?'

'The one – who whistled. Listen?'

The sound had moved from outside her window and grown fainter. She could scarcely hear it. It died away altogether. Then gaily it grew loud again as footsteps came down the passage.

> And if tis heaven's decree
> That mine she may not be,
> I'll never from the fair with life return . . .

Cathleen was clutching Miss O'Riordan's bony hand.

'It's the tinker! He's not dead at all!'

She felt the dry hand within hers tense. The door began to open. It was so dark that Cathleen could just discern the tall figure, the shock of dark hair, the gleam of white teeth.

'Well,' said Rory. 'How is she?'

Cathleen felt the tense fingers in hers relax.

'Only woken up in a state by all that noise you made,' Miss O'Riordan said severely. She stood up. Cathleen had the impression that she was soothing feathers that had ruffled in fright.

'Are you feeling better?' asked Rory, coming over to the bed.

Cathleen stared up into his dark face.

'That was the tinker's song you were whistling.'

'That? It's an old Irish ballad. The Snowy-breasted Pearl. I'm sorry. Did I startle you?'

'You did.'

'She isn't fit for visitors yet, Rory.'

Rory turned to his aunt.

'She needs a cup of tea. Why don't you go and make her one?' He sat on the side of the bed. 'I'm not a visitor.'

'The doctor gave strict instructions—'

Rory interrupted her firmly. 'Go and make that tea, Aunt Tilly. I'm not going to upset the patient.' He got up and flung open the window. 'I'm only going to let her breathe,' he said.

The mild evening air drifting on to her face was like a balm. Cathleen breathed deeply, relaxing. She was aware of the brief battle of wills that went on between the two. Then Aunt Tilly gave a snort and said angrily, 'I suppose you think you know best. I'm the one who's stayed awake for twenty-four hours.'

'Then you need tea, too,' said Rory. 'Run along.'

Aunt Tilly stalked away, muttering. Rory strolled back to the bed.

'I'm not going to upset you, Cathleen, but if you can, tell me what happened last night.'

It was easy enough to tell him, because he listened so intently, not indicating whether or not he believed her, but at least not deriding her story.

'You're sure about this baby's shoe?' he said at last.

'Yes. Your aunt suggests I've been associating it with my own baby and it's a kind of wishful thinking. But I am sure.'

'You didn't catch a glimpse of the person who – collided with you?'

He had been going to say 'pushed you'. Cathleen's breath caught for a moment, knowing he had almost put into words what she hadn't even dared to admit to herself.

'Not a sign. It happened so suddenly. He – the person – must have come out of the room just behind me. I didn't even hear a door open. But I did have the shoe in my hand, Rory. I did!'

He sat silent, his face telling nothing.

Then he said, almost irrelevantly, 'By the way, if you're

worried about that fracas over Peter Brady, the boy's all right. I went to Dublin yesterday and saw him.'

'That's where you went!'

His brows lifted ironically.

'Nice of you to notice I was away. Yes, I finally tracked down the Brady family. It took me eight hours. But the story was perfectly true. The father's a drunkard, and the mother – I'll give her the benefit of the doubt. She's warm-hearted enough. It seems they thought Peter might have a better chance if he were brought up in a religious atmosphere, but then they changed their minds. Brady said his wife was fretting for the boy. So rather than face the nuns who make him nervous, he planned a spot of kidnapping. Thoroughly enjoyed it, the rascal.'

Cathleen was gripping his arm.

'Rory, is that all?'

He looked down at her.

'No. It isn't all. But there's nothing in it to concern you. And I've also been over the west wing. The rooms are all empty.'

'Now, of course,' said Cathleen. She searched his face. 'Didn't you find anything at all?'

'I didn't get home until midnight. By that time the fuss was all over.'

'Oh, I see. By then there'd have been time – that's if I believe you.'

'Believe what you choose. But one thing you'd better do, and that is get away from here.'

'She's going,' came Miss O'Riordan's voice from the door.

The old lady came in carrying a teatray. She put it down with deliberation, and went on calmly, 'As soon as she can stand on her feet, she's going.'

Cathleen began to sit up.

'But what about the book?'

'I'll have to make other arrangements.'

'Aren't I satisfactory? Are you dismissing me?'

'I am. You haven't the right temperament. No one told me you had this distressing obsession.'

'What obsession?'

'About that tiresome infant of yours which you lost. I'd suggest a little psychiatric treatment before you attempt another job. Now don't get upset. My advice is meant for your own good.'

Not get upset when she was accused of being crazy! The anger flaming in Cathleen made the pain in her head so violent that she collapsed back on to the pillows.

You crafty old devil! she said. You're getting rid of me because I've stumbled on one of your secrets. And then you have the nerve to accuse me of being crazy.

She realized that none of the words had been said. Her lips refused to move. She could only stare up at the two faces above her, the one long-nosed, pallid, wickedly triumphant, the other – ah, no, Rory, you can't do that to me. You can't put me through all the anguish of coming back to life and then look sorry for me.

As if he read her thought; he turned abruptly and went out. Miss O'Riordan said firmly,

'Now, Mrs. Lamb, pull yourself together. Don't tell me you've been falling in love with my nephew Rory. That wouldn't do at all. Not at all.'

Not at all, not at all . . . The words faded and swelled and faded in her mind. She must have fallen asleep, or lost consciousness, for when she opened her eyes after what seemed to be only a moment her bedside light was on, and the curtains were drawn. And Liam was sitting beside her.

It was an enormous relief to see that Miss O'Riordan had gone. Cathleen smiled at Liam.

'I feel better,'

'Splendid. That was quite a fall you had.'

Cathleen moved cautiously, realizing for the first time her aching limbs. The pain was like an orchestra, the crashing drumbeats in her head now having subsided, the gentler more bearable sound of taut, strained muscles and nerves could be heard.

'Nothing's broken, is it?'

'No, lucky for you. We thought your skull was, at first. It really serves you right, you know, going prowling about like that in the dark.'

He had taken one of her hands in his and was gently stroking it. His fingers were soft-skinned, but curiously dry and hot, as if he were the one with a fever. Cathleen noticed the brightness of his eyes, too.

'You've been worried about me,' she said.

'You can say that again. But all's well that ends well. Aunt Tilly says you want to go back to England.'

'Does she?'

'Do you know, that's not a bad idea, because I'll be coming over shortly. I want to finish Red's training in England and get him thoroughly acclimatized. I'm going to sell the two colts and probably Macushla, if I can get a good enough offer for her, and sink everything on Red's chances.'

His fingers gripped hers.

'Meet me in London, Cathleen. I want you to. I love you. You do love me a little, don't you?'

Cathleen tried to concentrate, not on what he was saying but on the meaning beneath it. Was he planning to leave Loughneath Castle, to abandon Aunt Tilly and Rory to their secrets and start a new life in England?

Was this why he seemed so excited and feverish, his blue eyes blazing beneath their arched black brows? If he loved her, couldn't he do so here? Why had it to be in London?

'Why, of course I'll meet you in London some time,' she said vaguely. 'As it happens, your aunt—'

She never finished telling him that she was being igno-
miniously dismissed because at that moment Kitty burst
into the room, moving more quickly than Cathleen had ever
seen her move.

Her face was flaming, her eyes wild.

'Don't you dare do that, Liam! Don't you dare!'

CHAPTER SIXTEEN

LIAM turned in surprise.

'Goodness, Kitty, what do you think I'm planning to do?'

'You're planning to go to England with this woman and leave me here.'

'Don't call Cathleen "this woman",' Liam said irritably. 'And I'm not doing anything of the kind. I'm merely going to see a little of Cathleen when I'm there. Permissible?'

He was smiling placatingly, humouring Kitty who was so startlingly being a termagant. 'Come now, you knew I was going to run Red in the Grand National.'

'That doesn't mean going over months in advance!'

'Not months. But quite a time if the thing's to be done properly.'

Kitty's eyes smouldered.

'You mean you'll never come back.'

'Good heavens, whatever put that thought into your funny little head. You are in a state. Isn't she, Cathleen? Doesn't she look pretty like this? You know, if you stopped being so shy and nervous, Kitty, you'd have quite a lot of the O'Riordan looks.'

'You're only saying that! You've never meant any of the things you've said to me, except to get your own way. You don't care for me at all.'

'Kitty! Kitty! I adore you.' He put his hands at either side of her waist, and looked down at her indulgently. 'You're cute and I'd never leave you. I promise. If I go to England for more than a month I'll send for you. If Red wins the National we'll set London on fire. The handsome Liam O'Riordan and his charming sister . . .'

He was talking to her soothingly, beguilingly, almost like a lover ... The anger was going out of Kitty. She sagged against him. She seemed about to burst into tears.

Then she said inexplicably, 'Aunt Tilly always hated me. It's her fault I never had an operation for my hip. She was afraid mother would like me better than you. If I were a cripple, if mother could be made to believe that the operation would make the trouble much worse, then she might – she might do more for you. You were always Aunt Tilly's pet.'

Liam put his fingers over her lips.

'Shut up. You're talking nonsense. It was Cathleen who cracked her head, not you. And we shouldn't be upsetting her. Come along, there's a good girl. I'll get you a drink. Forgive us, Cathleen. I'll come back later.'

Cathleen closed her eyes. If she wasn't crazy already this family was making her so.

'I'd just like to be alone,' she said wearily.

Alone to take out Kitty's jealousy and turn it over, pondering its significance, the hold it had on Liam ... Who, perhaps, was just naturally kind-hearted to his handicapped sister, as he always had been, to inspire such devotion in her. Who surely couldn't be afraid of her ...

The gentle tap on the door made her start. Who, in this house, would have the courtesy to knock at the door of an invalid?

'Come in,' she said, and as if this were a film in which all the characters had to make a final bow, Magdalene Driscoll came in.

'The old bitch – sorry – Miss O'Riordan – didn't want to let me come up, but Rory said I could. I won't stay. You must be feeling terrible.'

Cathleen tried to laugh.

'I don't know which is the worst, coping with a cracked skull or this family.'

'I know. I do know.'

Although Magdalene's face was too thin and sharp, her eyes were beautiful, deep and sincere and full of light.

'Listen, I just thought you'd like to know that it's true Rory was with me the other night until pretty late.'

'The night the tinker was drowned?'

'Yes. I see you know what I mean. I'm not giving him an alibi because he doesn't need one. We were talking about a lot of things. And another thing, I'm not in love with him. Maybe I could be, but it wouldn't be much use. He's in love with someone else.'

She shrugged, her mouth turned down philosophically. 'I just thought I'd tell you. Now look after yourself. Don't be scared away by that old bee in a bottle. This place has had happy days as well as bad ones, you know.'

'But I'm leaving anyway,' Cathleen said.

'Are you then? What a pity. Then take your time getting well enough to travel.'

She went to the door, giving a little wave of her hand. Her face was gay.

'Goodbye now. Good luck.'

'But the baby!' Cathleen cried passionately.

Magdalene paused. 'Forget it. Shamus never had a child.'

It was at this stage that Cathleen knew she must be delirious. Could all those people have been in her room and said so many strange things to her? She must sleep, and wake clear-headed. Otherwise she would never know what had been going on, never find out about the baby's shoe. Oh, the little shoe, so forever empty because Debby . . .

There were tears on her cheeks as she fell asleep. She didn't know who else came in to look at her, but someone did, because when she woke much later the light had been turned out and the room was so quiet it was heaven.

The door handle was rattling softly.

'Mrs. Lamb! Mrs. Lamb, are you awake?'

It was the voice of Peggy Moloney with its caressing brogue. It was just growing light. Cathleen sat up, feeling weak but marvellously clear-headed. Whatever sedatives she had been filled with yesterday had worn off, and now she could think again.

'Come in, Peggy.'

'I can't. The door's locked.'

Cathleen started up.

'It can't be.'

'Did you lock yourself in? I don't blame you.'

To her great relief, Cathleen found she was able to walk. She was stiff and sore, but mobile.

It was true enough that the door was locked, and that the key had been taken away. What had they been afraid she might do? Prowl again, stumble on things she shouldn't know?

Peggy, on the other side of the door, was giggling, but with a touch of hysteria.

'It's Miss O'Riordan,' she whispered through the keyhole. 'She said she was going to sit with my patient all night. She couldn't be in two places at once. I suppose she thought you might tumble down a staircase again.'

'It's monstrous,' said Cathleen angrily. 'Why does she have to sit with Mrs. O'Riordan anyway?'

'Because the poor thing's been trying to talk. She's been saying that "lie, lie" again. The old dragon is afraid she might miss something if she goes away. She's fallen asleep sitting up in her chair so I slipped down to see you. I wanted to come yesterday and look after you, but they wouldn't let me.'

'I'm not going to be locked in,' Cathleen said fiercely. 'I won't stand it. I'll wake the whole house.'

She began rattling the doorknob and thumping with her fists.

Peggy giggled again on the high note of hysteria.

'Be careful, Mrs. Lamb. After concussion you're supposed to rest.'

'But not to be kept a prisoner! Peggy, go and wake someone.'

'Sure,' said Peggy doubtfully. 'Who?'

A door opened somewhere and there were footsteps.

'You don't need to wake anyone, nurse. I've got the key.' It was Kitty's voice, cold and hostile.

'I don't know what you're doing down here disturbing Mrs. Lamb so early.'

'I don't know why she has to be locked in,' Peggy retorted.

'Because she was wandering in her head last night. It was for her own safety.'

The door opened and both girls stood there.

'How are you feeling, Mrs. Lamb?' Peggy asked solicitously. 'You don't look so bad now.'

'No. I'm much better.'

'The doctor said you had to rest,' Kitty said stonily.

'I have. I've slept for about forty hours.'

'But however did you fall down those stairs?' Peggy asked. 'Had you been having something out of Miss O'Riordan's bottle—' She clapped her hand to her mouth, looking at Kitty.

Cathleen answered very soberly, 'I wasn't drunk, I was pushed.'

'*Pushed!*' Now Peggy was too startled to worry about her previous levity.

'She stumbled in the dark,' said Kitty coldly. 'Ask my aunt. She found her. You see, we weren't joking when we said it had affected her head. Pushed, indeed!'

It was not the first fall she had had, Cathleen was thinking. There had been the other one, off Macushla who had been startled. She made a shot in the dark.

'Have you always been jealous of Liam's girl-friends?' she asked Kitty. 'I can't be the first one he's looked at. What did you do about the others? Did you succeed in driving them away?'

Kitty's eyes went wide and expressionless. It was a defence she had, that baby look, for there was nothing babyish in her complete control of herself.

'Liam hasn't had any other girl-friends,' she said. 'He loves nothing but his horses. You might be interested to know that he only admires you because you look well on a horse. Otherwise he'd have taken no notice of you. Beyond being pleasant, of course. He has much better manners than Rory. If it's women-friends you're interested in, Rory's the one you want to investigate.'

Bigamy would be the last thing this family needs . . . But to which nephew was Miss O'Riordan referring? Kitty turned her cool gaze to Peggy.

'If you want to be of use, nurse, you might go down and make Mrs. Lamb some tea. Otherwise she might collapse again and have even stranger fancies. She seems to think we've been hiding a baby in the west wing. My aunt says she must see a psychiatrist when she goes back to London.'

Cathleen wanted to make a heated retort to that, but sheer physical weakness overcame her. The pain was thumping in her head again, making everything a dream. She let Peggy help her back to bed, and lay with her eyes closed miserably. She was a fool to antagonize Kitty. Kitty had an unexpected core of strength, and where Liam was concerned it was obvious she would lie, steal, perhaps even kill.

I would do anything in the world for you . . . That wasn't Kitty, it was her mother writing to her father. But it showed the same tenacious, unreasoning loyalty.

This explained nothing of the immediate problem. The existence of the baby's shoe . . .

Cathleen lay wondering whether there was any use in

making this revelation to Peggy. Peggy was a sane young creature, but she was a rumour bearer, all the same. And was it wise to involve her in possible danger?

Danger! That was the first time Cathleen had admitted that fact to herself. She knew now, very soberly, why everyone said she must go, even Liam with his more subtle suggestion to meet her in London. If she remained something would have to be done to stop her compulsive activities. Because she wouldn't be able to stop them herself, not while she knew there had to be a foot to fit that small shoe, there had to be ears to hear the nursery rhyme, there had to be a reason for a night-light . . .

Peggy came back with a breakfast tray. Her cheeks were pink with excitement.

'The police are back! Two of them. They've asked for Mr. Rory and Mr. Liam. I wanted to stop and listen but Mary Kate shoo'd me off. I only just heard them saying that they'd found out the tinker's name wasn't Danny King but Danny Regan, and he had a wife somewhere about here, but they can't locate her.'

Cathleen was out of bed and pulling on her dressing-gown.

Peggy's voice came from a long distance.

'Mrs. Lamb! Sure and you're not strong enough to go downstairs. The police wouldn't be wanting you.'

Regan! The name was shouting in her mind. Moira Regan! Danny must be a relation of Moira's. Her brother, perhaps. He was seeking to claim her rights from the O'Riordan family. So he had died . . .

'Mrs. Lamb! You're as white as a sheet.'

'I'm all *right*,' Cathleen said irritably. 'Just let me go.'

The two policemen, a sergeant and a constable, were in the library. Now it was Cathleen instead of Kitty who was listening at doors. She had to grip the doorpost as she heard Rory saying in his level voice,

'But you have no actual proof that Eileen Burke was his wife?'

'No proof, sir. Just a matter of deduction. Mrs. Murphy saw the tinker calling on her a couple of times, once in the morning and once after dark. But she admits he may have been trying to sell Mrs. Burke something. On the other hand, Mrs. Murphy says this woman was usually pretty sharp at sending people about their business, but the tinker's visits were quite lengthy. Moreover, just as he meets with his death, Mrs. Burke disappears, telling no one she was leaving.'

'Then she'll have to be found, won't she?' Liam said.

'She'll be found, sir, sooner or later. We were wondering if either of you gentlemen could give us a lead.'

There was the smallest silence.

Then, with a hint of anger, Liam said, 'Because her husband, if he was her husband, had the misfortune to die on our property, I don't see why you should think we're concealing a distraught woman. I should think she'd be glad to see the end of him, if you ask me.'

'Don't get me wrong, sir. But Danny King, or Danny Regan, wasn't the only caller Mrs. Burke had. Did either of you gentlemen happen to know her?'

'Never set eyes on her,' said Liam.

'And you, sir?'

Cathleen stopped breathing.

'I know who she was, of course,' Rory answered. 'She had a child, hadn't she?'

'A boy of about two years.'

'Have you checked trains and buses?'

'That, naturally, is being attended to,' said the sergeant in a pained voice. 'There'll also be a notice in the newspapers. But we're making urgent inquiries about here.'

'Urgent?' said Liam.

'We feel the matter may be urgent, sir,' said the sergeant

pompously. 'If anything comes to your memory that you think may be of importance I'd ask you to get in touch with the station.'

'Where are you searching?' Rory asked.

'There's a lot of bog country around here,' the sergeant said vaguely. 'Nasty stuff to get lost in.'

Cathleen didn't wait to hear any more. She was almost certain she knew where the missing Eileen Burke and her child were. She must find them before the police left. Mrs. Burke must be told that she was in deadly danger. If her husband could be silenced by means of an accident, so could she, all too easily. A fall down the stairs, for instance . . .

The passages and the staircase leading to the west wing were so long. At the top of the stairs Cathleen had to pause to get her breath, and will herself not to collapse. The pain throbbed in her temples. She shouldn't have attempted to come up here alone. But if she had burst into the library with her fantastic suggestion, Rory or Liam or both of them would have laughed scornfully, would have told the police that unfortunately she had had a nasty crack on the head which had made her temporarily of unsound mind . . .

And there would have been just enough delay for someone to hide the furtive guests.

In a moment now the suspense would be over. She had only to go quickly from door to door, looking into the empty rooms until she found the one that wasn't empty.

It was impossible to believe that they were all empty. Finally, she stood in dismay in the last one, looking at the bare floor, the shape of a bed and other furniture humped under dusty covers. There was no one up here. Even when she called no one answered.

A baby would have been awake and making sounds at this hour.

The only sound was the harsh cawing of the crows, the

far-off sound of a car engine starting, the bang of a door. The police had gone.

It came to her that the rooms were uncannily quiet. If Eileen Burke, who was not a meek person, had been held against her will she might have had to be controlled.

Cathleen stared fascinatedly at the covers over the furniture, at the large wardrobe, fast shut. Could she bring herself to look under the dusty covers or open that door? There were places of concealment in the other rooms, too. One would have to start a systematic search.

Tentatively she turned the handle of the wardrobe door. Something billowed at her out of the dark. She stepped back, stifling a scream, and a hand caught her wrist.

'Ghosts?' said Liam pleasantly.

She could hardly speak. She scarcely knew which was the most frightening, the dark forgotten garment that had seemed to fly out as she touched it, or Liam's hard grip round her waist.

'You scared me! You came without a sound.'

'I heard someone up here. I thought it might be you. Aunt Tilly said you needed watching. I didn't believe her until now.' His blue eyes looked down at her. 'My poor darling!'

Cathleen wrenched away from him. Did he think her *mad*?

'You won't find your baby up here,' he said with the greatest gentleness. 'She's in England, don't you remember?'

'Stop it, Liam!' she said furiously. 'You know it isn't Debby I'm looking for. It's Danny Regan's baby. That's the one there's been all the fuss about, isn't it? Not Moira's at all.'

She had been making a wild guess. But now, from Liam's still face and his watchful eyes, she seemed to be getting near the truth.

'Moira never did have a baby, did she?'

'How would I know? She was my brother's wife.'

'But you knew about Danny and what he was doing, didn't you? Blackmailing your aunt. Making her sell all her valuables, so he – why, I don't believe he was getting the money at all!'

She was staring beyond Liam at the other figure in the doorway.

'You're both in it!' she whispered.

Rory strode over to her, took her shoulders and shook her violently.

'You're not a fool! Don't behave like one. Are you coming with me to try to find this woman?'

Cathleen blinked away tears of shock and pain. She had to cling to Rory simply because she couldn't stand upright.

She heard Liam saying, 'Are you going to do the police's work for them? Can't you see what's happened? The woman's been in this with her husband. Naturally she's got away while she could.'

'All the more reason to find her before the police do.'

'You're a fool. It's a bit late now to protect the family from scandal. Or is it yourself you're protecting?'

'We'll see,' said Rory levelly. 'Cathleen! Are you coming?'

She didn't know Liam had gone until she saw that the room was empty except for herself and Rory. His face above hers was without any kind of tenderness. She was recovering from the effects of her accident and could hardly stand. Yet she knew she was going with him.

'I can dress in five minutes.'

'Good. I'll be waiting.'

The long journey back to her room and the effort of dressing should have enfeebled her more, but now some inner strength had come to her and even her hands were steady.

When she went downstairs again Rory was waiting for

her, and Mary Kate had just brought in a pot of coffee.

'There it is, sir. And is it planning to kill the poor girl you are, taking her out in that condition?'

'Drink this,' Rory said, pouring out a cup of coffee and handing it to Cathleen. 'I hope Mary Kate isn't speaking the truth. But I need you. It's the first time I've believed in a woman's intuition.'

'I suppose it's because of my own baby,' Cathleen said dully. 'It seems to give me a sixth sense. Do you think I'm right in saying Moira never had a baby?'

'I think you may be right. We'll talk about that later.'

Cathleen sipped the coffee and the pain in her head ceased to be such a tumult, but merely thumped steadily like a ponderous clock.

'Have you found out what your aunt and your sister know?'

'My aunt and my sister can be wonderful liars when they choose. They swear there have been no guests in the west wing, or anywhere else. They may even be speaking the truth.'

'The baby's shoe—'

'They say you had an hallucination. We'll talk in the car. Are you ready?'

Cathleen nodded. She was aware of Mary Kate's horrified gaze following her. Why, the funny old woman thought she was going to disappear, too, like Eileen Burke.

Rory opened the door of the car. She climbed in, wrapping her coat round her against the chill of the morning. He started the car and turned it expertly in the narrow drive.

'Thanks for coming with me.'

'It doesn't mean I trust you.'

'I thought that was exactly what it did mean.'

She looked at him silently, not trying any more to read his unreadable face.

'To be honest, I didn't want to leave you in the house. And don't imagine, for sweet heaven's sake, that that means I want to get you at my mercy. Unless,' he added, 'you would like it that way.'

'I'm not in the mood for jokes.'

'That wasn't a joke. Haven't you noticed that we're not a joking family? All these wild melodramatic threats aren't threats at all. They're actual happenings. We don't talk about hypothetical skeletons in cupboards. There really are skeletons, bones and all.'

Cathleen huddled into her coat.

'Is this why you're in such a hurry to find Eileen Burke?'

He didn't answer at once. He was driving very fast, the stone walls going by in a flickering blur. There was drizzle in the air, and a low grey sky. It was a mournful morning, all too suited to their apprehensive mood.

'I think Eileen Burke can save her own skin,' he said at last. 'It's yours I'm worrying about.'

CHAPTER SEVENTEEN

RORY stopped outside the hotel. There was nobody about in the little town. For once they had evaded the loungers and the starers. The street was quiet and grey and empty.

Rory rang the bell, and after a long time Mrs. Murphy, in a shabby cardigan and skirt and bedroom slippers, opened the door.

'Good morning,' Rory said with his rare charming smile. 'Any chance of some coffee? We have a long journey to make.'

The woman looked past him to Cathleen. She smiled, more shyly than grudgingly.

'I expect it's something stronger than coffee you want. 'You'd better come in the dining-room. We've had no peace around here since Mrs. Burke disappeared.'

'We want to talk about her,' said Rory.

'Do you then? I thought you would. Well, I can't tell you anything except that the baby cried a lot that night. My room faces her house. I can't help hearing.'

'You didn't hear anybody come late?'

'No. Not a soul. And I didn't hear her go. She'd have to wheel the pram over the cobblestones, and I don't sleep that well. I can't think why I wouldn't have heard.'

'She could have left by the back way?'

Mrs. Murphy looked up suspiciously.

'If she had a car. It could come up the lane. You know that as well as I do. If she was catching a train or a bus she'd have gone by the front. Anyway, the first bus isn't till seven and she must have been gone by then.'

'So she was getting ready to leave when the baby was crying?'

'I didn't say that.'

'What time was it?'

'About two o'clock, I'd say. And that's all I can tell you.' Her face was closed and sulky again. 'I didn't fancy Mrs. Burke as a neighbour and I don't want to be mixed up in any of her doings. All those cheap beads and ear-rings, like a gipsy. She didn't belong here. She never once went to Mass, did you know? I'll get your coffee. It was Irish you wanted, wasn't it?'

'Thank you, Mrs. Murphy. I'll say a prayer for you.'

'But do you know – ' the woman had come back to say in a scandalized voice, '– there's some say she helped her husband to fall in that lake. Fancy that now! I wouldn't be surprised at all – her telling lies that he was in India, and all the time he was peddling pots and kettles. How do you know who you can trust, tell me that.'

'Mrs. Murphy's got quite talkative,' said Cathleen, not looking at Rory.

'A little scandal's a great loosener of the tongue. So, I hope, is her Irish coffee.'

'Why?'

'Because I want you to tell me why you don't trust me.'

'Rory – there's no time for that now.'

'There's time.'

She was forced to answer. His eyes never left her face.

'I don't think I trust anyone in your house. Certainly not your aunt, certainly not Kitty. Liam, I'm not sure – I think he has some kind of private obsession, just as you all have. And you – Magdalene Driscoll says you're in love with someone else, and love can make anyone a bit crazy, but more especially – and don't tell me I'm wrong – an O'Riordan. So!' She shrugged.

'Then am I a bit crazy,' said Rory, 'for wanting you out of that house? Even if you do babble about babies' shoes, and that I find an enormous bore, if you don't mind my saying so. But I assure you I want you here with me, right now.'

He gave her his charming, deliberate smile. She met it with a cool stare.

'You just want your own way about something. You're talking to me the way Liam did to Kitty last night.'

'Did he, then?' Rory said thoughtfully. 'But Kitty's his sister, which is different.'

'You're in love with someone.' It must be her aching head that was making her lose her ability to keep to the main point of an argument. This remark was irrelevant. 'Magdalene said—'

'And would Magdalene know? And were we talking about love?'

He wouldn't let her escape his gaze. She flushed, and welcomed the arrival of Mrs. Murphy with steaming cups of coffee smelling strongly of whisky. She thanked Mrs. Murphy, and abruptly changed the subject.

'Rory, there *is* a baby!'

'Oh, sure. Ireland's full of them. Then drink your coffee and we'll find this elusive baby, and it's not mine, I'm telling you.'

'Nor Shamus's?'

'Nor Shamus's.'

'You know this for certain?'

'Drink your coffee,' he said. 'You're going to need it, since you insist on finding out unpleasant information. Here's some more. Moira Regan, or more accurately Moira O'Riordan, is dead. She drowned herself precisely eight weeks ago in the Liffey. She was childless. There was no fuss about her death. Her family knew, but kept it from us, perhaps understandably. What had we ever done for her?'

'Oh, no!' whispered Cathleen, and remembered suddenly the grey water of the Liffey slipping beneath the humped stone bridges, and the old woman saying 'Red hair turns black in water . . .'

'I told you you wouldn't like it.' He wasn't being facetious now. He looked tired. There were deep lines in his face and a grim set to his mouth.

'How long have you known this?'

'Since yesterday, when I was in Dublin. I made progress yesterday, first with that scoundrel Regan—'

'Regan!'

'Yes, another Regan. Calling himself Brady this time. Another loyal brother of Moira's. They were all in for the plucking of the goose, all right. This fine specimen lent his youngest child to the Mary and Joseph orphanage – sold would have been a better word – until his conscience bothered him too much.'

'You mean that a child had to be produced, otherwise your aunt couldn't be blackmailed?'

'Exactly. Aunt Tilly is much too shrewd to be blackmailed over a child she's never seen. And it had to be the right age, presuming Shamus had had a son. Having it put in the orphanage must have been one of her conditions.'

'Of course!' Cathleen exclaimed. 'The man she was talking to on the telephone in Dublin that day must have been one of the brothers. But wasn't he terribly careless, leaving that bit of torn letter in the bar for anyone to read.'

'He was a careless fellow,' said Rory. 'He drank too much and let himself get drowned. The letter must have been to his wife, waiting for him in Loughneath. He tore it up, so his heart couldn't have been in the business.'

Cathleen remembered the blithe whistle of the tinker. He had been a likeable rogue. Perhaps his heart hadn't been in the plot. Perhaps his greedy wife had been pushing him on . . .

'But, Rory, if this is all true, can't you get your aunt to talk? She must be terribly worried and frightened, especially when she thought it was only the tinker wanting money from her, and now there's someone else. The brother in Dublin, I suppose.'

'No,' said Rory slowly. 'Not him. He was not only scared to the depths of his soul by Danny's death, but he swore on everything holy – and an Irishman doesn't do that lightly – that he had had nothing more to do with it.'

Cathleen met his eyes. 'Then who? Your aunt must talk.'

'You try to make her. I spent until midnight with her last night. She won't admit a thing. She says she wanted that five hundred pounds for gambling. Nothing else. The anonymous letters she had been receiving spreading scandalous rumours she burnt, which is the only way to treat such documents. And moreover, if Shamus's wife is dead, it's good riddance.'

'She can't be as hard as that! She must be desperately worried. I told you, I saw her face yesterday when she got another letter.'

'Then whatever she's hiding must be even more frightening,' Rory said. 'The old fool! The magnificent old fool! She faces this the way my father faced the British Army!'

'Someone's baby was in the castle,' Cathleen insisted. 'If your aunt doesn't know about it, then it must be Kitty who does. It must have been Kitty who pushed me down the stairs and then rushed down and took the baby's shoe out of my hand, so that no one would believe me when I told them about it.' Cathleen stood up urgently. 'We've got to find this woman, this Eileen Burke.'

'I agree. Let's go.'

He put some money on the table for Mrs. Murphy. They went out into the thickening drizzle. The little lakes in the Connemara bogs wouldn't be blue today, but a stormier grey than the sky. The grey of the wet donkeys pulling the turf-cutter's carts with their load of neat black peat slabs.

'Where are you going?' Cathleen asked, as Rory started the car. 'Have you the same idea as the police?' She spoke the words apprehensively. 'The bogs?'

'No. I have another theory. If it's true we won't find Eileen Burke drowned in any bog.'

Cathleen clung to his arm, shivering. 'Rory – the real secret is nothing to do with a child, is it?'

His jaw was hard, his eyes narrowed and cold.

'Didn't I tell you our skeletons all have X certificates?'

They had to leave the car on the roadside and cross a boggy field.

'It's all part of the estate,' Rory said. 'It's much shorter across country.'

'It's near the lake,' Cathleen said instinctively, and fearfully.

'Yes. It's a turf-cutter's cabin. Hasn't been lived in for years. We used to play in it as boys.'

The tumbledown cabin with its thatched roof was picturesque against the green hillside. It wasn't until one was close that the gaping windows and the holes in the roof were apparent. The door sagged half-open across a dark damp threshold.

Rory pushed it open and disappeared into the gloom. For a moment Cathleen couldn't force herself to follow him. She waited, holding her breath, expecting some exclamation, expecting what?

But in a moment he called, 'Aren't you coming in? It's dark, but you'll get used to it in a minute or two.'

Then, as she stepped gingerly through the doorway, he did give an exclamation.

'That's interesting. Look!'

She blinked, trying to see what he pointed to in the corner by the hearth. It shone faintly. It was a small collection of tin pots and pans.

'The tinker!' she whispered.

'Exactly. He must have been sleeping here. There's been a fire quite recently.' He stirred the ashes with his foot. a very faint smoke rose. 'Very recently,' he said thoughtfully.

Cathleen was looking at the wooden bunk, the sod floor dampened in circles where the rain dripped through the lamentable roof. That brown-faced bright-eyed man, so alive, so virile, must have thought the rewards were going to be sufficient to compensate for living in this discomfort. But no doubt he sneaked a few warm hours with his wife at nights. Had she known this was his hide-out, had she visited him here?

But certainly she had. For here, tucked at the side of the bunk, almost invisible against the crumbling wall, was a woman's handkerchief.

Cathleen snatched it out. It had a little blood on it, dried brown.

'Rory!'

He took it from her, studying it. Then he began poking in the ashes with a stick.

'This fire hasn't been out for more than twenty-four hours. It's still warm. It looks as if – '

'As if what?' Cathleen cried in an agony.

'As if some kind of material has been burnt on it. Look, that ash isn't peat. What would you say it was?'

'Something woollen,' said Cathleen, her lips stiff.

'Something with blood on it,' said Rory. 'She had been hurt.'

'She?'

'Who else? She was hurt, she couldn't look after her baby, it had to either be taken to the castle or left to bawl its head off or starve. She came here because she thought her husband had sent for her, she didn't know he was dead. But when she got here there was – someone else. Someone who said if she didn't agree to the new plans her baby would never come back.'

'What are you saying?' Cathleen whispered.

'Look!' said Rory, pointing to the wall. 'It's a bit dark. But can you read that? We wrote the names when we were kids playing here. Shamus, Rory, Liam.'

Cathleen stared at the names scratched with a burnt stick on the wall.

'But Liam is there twice. Once at the bottom—'

'In his correct place. Once at the top where he longed to be. He was a jealous youngster, Liam, particularly of Shamus. Not so much of me until Shamus died.'

Cathleen stared, not speaking.

'Look again,' said Rory. 'The name at the top has been gone over.' He rubbed with his finger. 'Very recently. I think, you know, it might be the only clue Eileen Burke could give us.'

'But where is she now?'

'I should think she's perfectly all right, wherever she is. She's got her baby back, you see. Which means she must have agreed to the new plan, and perhaps not too unwillingly at that, now she's had time to think things over. After all, Danny drank too much and dragged her down, and who knows, she might be ambitious enough to think that one day her son will really be the heir to the castle. Two can play at this game, this low-down rotten game. Let's get home. Someone's got to be made to talk.'

'But will they? Any of them?' Cathleen thought of Kitty, of Miss O'Riordan and her relentless vigil, of Liam telling her her fall had affected her brain . . . The O'Riordans stuck together, guarding their secrets.

'Wouldn't it be the logical thing to find Eileen Burke now we've got this far?'

'No,' he said strangely. 'I've found out all I need to about that part of the affair.'

'What do you mean? Aren't you looking for the baby at all?'

'Baby, baby, baby! It's only you who's been fooled by that red herring.'

She shrank away from his hard eyes.

'I've been waiting a long time,' he said, very quietly, 'to find this out.'

'To find what out?'

'Why, Mrs. Lamb, you're not as bright as usual. The truth about my brother Shamus's death, of course.'

CHAPTER EIGHTEEN

A WHITE face moved away from the window as they drove up. Kitty in her eternal role of the watcher, the listener. She came out to meet them.

'Where have you been? Aunt Tilly is furious. She says if Mrs. Lamb is well enough to go gadding about the country, she's well enough to get on with her work.'

She spoke directly to Rory, not looking at Cathleen.

Cathleen said, 'But I thought I'd been sacked.'

'You have been,' said Rory. 'You're getting away from here.'

'Rory!' That was Miss O'Riordan's harsh voice coming from the shadows of the hall. 'I won't have you interfering in my affairs. If I'm forced to change my mind about Mrs. Lamb's value to me, it's none of your business.'

She crossed over to them. She was wearing the shabby tweed suit that today seemed to hang even more loosely on her broomstick figure. Her hair was pinned up inadequately, as if she had done it hastily without brushing it. Patches of rouge on her high cheekbones gave her an appearance of spectral animation.

'Does it occur to you, Aunt Tilly,' Rory said, 'that Mrs. Lamb may not want to stay? She hardly bargained for these happenings when she took the job.'

'If you mean by "these happenings" her hallucinations, they're her affair, aren't they? She'd have them, wherever she was. Even, I've no doubt, in an English vicarage. They're something she's got to fight. Don't you agree, Mrs. Lamb?' The heavily-lidded glittering eyes were on Cathleen now. 'You can't dismiss a nightmare by running away from it, can you? That's when you have it with you forever.'

'I'll be very glad to stay,' Cathleen said unhesitatingly. 'Thank you for letting me.'

'Only because there's no one else and I'm short of time. These things have to be recorded.'

For a moment Aunt Tilly brooded, and Cathleen was quite sure she wasn't thinking of anything mentioned in the collection of letters and anecdotes. What she referred to was inside her own head, her private nightmare.

'Get out, Cathleen,' Rory said. 'This is no place for strangers.'

Strangers! Cathleen was deeply hurt. It was Liam who came to her defence. He was dressed, as almost always, in riding clothes. He looked slim and handsome, his eyes sparkling.

'They're only using you, Cathleen. Aunt Tilly on this absurd book of hers, Rory on a wild-goose chase for a woman who's probably crossed the Irish sea by now. Am I right?'

Rory answered levelly, 'You might know better than me. We've merely established that the woman you're talking about kept a rendezvous with her husband in that old cabin. You remember? Where we used to play as boys.'

'More deduction?' said Liam.

'Oh, no, it was clear enough. The tinker seems to have been a violent chap. There's evidence she was knocked about a bit. Perhaps he deserved to be pushed in the pool.'

'You think his wife – killed him?' That was Kitty, a macabre undercurrent of eagerness in her voice.

'Perhaps. Perhaps it was an accident. Anyway, she was well enough to get away. Liam may be right. She may be in England by now. Weren't you talking of going over, Liam?'

Play it cool, thought Cathleen. Those might have been

Rory's unspoken words to her. She listened, watching the brothers.

'I'm hoping to take Red over for the Grand National, yes. In a few months' time. What's that got to do with it?'

'I understood Kitty thought it was to be much sooner than that. Didn't you, Kitty?'

Kitty flashed a look at Liam. She could control her voice, but not her colour. The bright scarlet flowed in her cheeks.

'Good gracious, we weren't being serious. Liam simply said it was time I had some fun. This year, next year, I don't care.'

'Liam's perfectly right,' said Aunt Tilly unexpectedly. 'It is time Kitty came out of that ridiculous shell. Haven't I been telling her so for long enough? No interest in clothes, no interest in men. Heavens, the girl isn't normal. I tell you what, we'll arrange a dance. She can go to Dublin and buy a new dress. Mrs. Lamb, you might be good enough to take her and give her some advice. Your taste seems sound enough.'

Had everyone gone mad? They were supposed to be talking about a missing woman, a possible murder, and here they were chatting about parties and clothes. To Kitty's intense misery, and Liam's obvious mystification. It wasn't possible to read Rory's thoughts. He seemed diverted more than anything else by his unpredictable aunt.

'She can wear her mother's rubies,' said Aunt Tilly. 'After all, they'll be hers soon enough.'

'Surely not!' Liam exclaimed. 'They're an heirloom. Won't they belong to – Rory's wife?'

Aunt Tilly gave him a curious long look.

'You were going to say Shamus's wife, weren't you? And of course she should have had them, if she'd behaved like any normal wife. But since she's out of the picture, I'm quite certain Cecilia would want Kitty to have them. Oh, be bothered as to whether that procedure is correct by law, or not. I say it should be done and I hope neither of you boys will disagree with me.'

The red flags of colour had left Kitty's face.

'Do you really think mother would like me to have them?'

She was suddenly very young and piteous. She was reading into this the gesture of love which apparently she had always been denied.

'Of course she would,' said Aunt Tilly, with emphasis.

'Then that's final,' said Rory. 'I endorse it. And since it's my wife who will be the loser, I'm making quite a sacrifice. It hardly affects you, Liam.'

Liam was slapping his riding crop against his leg. He did it as if something were irritating him.

All Cathleen could think was that this extraordinary family lived in near poverty while sitting on a collection of jewels worth a fortune. The Fabergé brooch, now these extraordinary rubies . . .

'Look here,' said Aunt Tilly, beginning to stride up and down. 'Why don't we shake ourselves out of these doldrums? Why don't we have a party tonight? After all, that dreary tinker and his wife were nothing to us. We don't have to go into mourning for them. Let's have some gaiety.'

'Tonight?' said Liam.

'Now, if we could rustle up some guests. But you can't dress for dinner at ten in the morning, and if Kitty's to wear the rubies, she must have bare shoulders.'

'Aunt Tilly—'

'Now let's see who to ask.' The extraordinary old woman was in her element, striding up and down, clapping her bony palms together, eyes snapping, hair awry. 'Magdalene, that dreary old bore, Colonel Green, the Hunters, the McDirmids, who's that young man who bought the O'Connal place, Rory? Kitty might find him interesting. We might dance a little, eh? Paddy O'Grady could play the fiddle.'

'You've gone mad,' Liam exclaimed.

'Not a bit of it, not a bit of it. Did we never give a ball at Loughneath Castle? Not perhaps at such short notice, but that will make it more amusing. The best parties are always the impromptu ones. There's plenty of whisky, isn't there? What more do we want?'

'Aunt Tilly!' Kitty was clutching at an irrelevancy. 'How can I wear the rubies without a suitable dress?'

'I've one,' said Cathleen. 'A green silk. It would suit you. It may need a little alteration. You're so slim.'

A look of aversion, or was it shame, came into Kitty's eyes. Before she could protest Aunt Tilly gave Cathleen a hearty slap across the shoulders.

'Splendid, Mrs. Lamb, splendid. I knew you'd be our sort when you got rid of your morbid fancies. Ready for a party at a moment's notice. We'll all forget our troubles tonight. No sick, no orphaned, no dying. Liam! You seem worried. You haven't any other engagement, have you?'

'No, I haven't, but the whole countryside will think you've gone mad.'

'Perhaps I have, dear boy. Perhaps I have.'

'You've had two nights with almost no sleep. You should be resting.'

'I'll rest, all in good time.' She lifted her shoulders in a gesture of anger. 'Did you think I was in my dotage? I believe you did. That's the only explanation for it all.'

Once again she was making an ordinary statement cover a private thought.

It was Liam whose eyes fell beneath her contemptuous regard.

Cathleen had the opportunity for only a word with Rory.

'Now you won't insist on my going?' She hadn't meant to plead. Her voice sounded aggressive.

'You don't want to miss the fun?'

'Fun!'

'For the onlooker,' Rory said pointedly.

'Rory, the old girl's gone off her head,' Liam said angrily. 'A party in the castle tonight, with the police hanging round half the time!'

'Suggest to them that Eileen Burke's in England,' Rory said lightly. 'They'll be interested in your line of reasoning. By the way, this seems to be a free-for-all. I'm sure Aunt Tilly will have no objection to whom we ask.'

'What exactly do you mean by that?'

Cathleen had turned to go. Rory took her arm. The light proprietary touch both annoyed her and held her rigid. She thought she was tired of being ordered about by Rory O'Riordan.

'What about your girl friend in Loughneath?'

'What on earth are you talking about?'

'Don't tell me that's over already. You were easily enough persuaded not to go to Dublin the other night when I threatened to tell Cathleen about your other feminine interest.'

'You rotten cad!' Liam's eyes were blazing. 'You only made a guess.'

'But you stayed home. Remember?'

'It suited me to. And if you think I'm asking a village girl to this ridiculous party, you have another thought coming.'

He strode away, his head high, the younger brother in a familiar pattern of pique and humiliation.

'Rory! That wasn't fair.'

'What is fair?' He looked at her with his hard, black gaze. Then he laughed suddenly, his face taking on its miraculous look of easy charm.

'So, to the jewels and fine linen. You might save the first dance for me.'

'Is your aunt serious?'

'Never more so, if I know Aunt Tilly.' He seemed subtly happier, less tense and wary. 'You'd better stay,' he said abruptly. 'I think it will be all right now.' He ruffled her hair. It was the briefest gesture. 'I'm sorry about the rubies,' he said inexplicably. And was gone.

The only thing that was clear now to Cathleen was that it was Liam who had made the furtive telephone call in the library that night. And that Kitty, his supporter as always, had with surprising presence of mind diverted Cathleen. But lately Kitty had been more frightened than loyal. She was sure of that, too.

After the mad day of preparation it was time to dress. All Miss O'Riordan's invitations had been accepted. People, apparently, would drop anything to come to an impromptu party at the castle. Magdalene Driscoll had been the most eager, for she had arrived half an hour too early. Cathleen had watched her car drive up, and seen her, tall and elegant, with her swathed red hair, climb out and wave to someone in the doorway.

Had Rory asked her to come early? Cathleen, who hadn't begun to dress, thought of them having a quiet drink together. Suddenly she was as loath as Kitty to go downstairs. It had been all right during the day, while they had all helped to clean and polish, to prepare food in the large, cool, dark kitchen where Mary Kate was a whirlwind, rising to the occasion with true Irish zest for a party, and later to alter the green dress for Kitty to wear. There had been no time to think. It had even been fun. She had thought that this place was too haunted ever to be light-hearted. By some miracle she had succeeded in shutting out thoughts of everything but the immediate task.

It was only in the last half-hour that her tension had returned overwhelmingly. Perhaps it was because the light was fading and the grey evening had its familiar melan-

choly, the trees dripping in the light rain, the crows returning to haggle and squabble for room to roost on the overloaded tree.

Something was going to happen this evening. The party
was only a bright façade for something else. The bones
were showing through the skeleton's pretty face. Aunt Tilly
had said, 'What time does it get dark?' and everyone had
argued about the exact time, depending on the fineness of
the evening, no one thinking to wonder why Aunt Tilly had
asked such a strange question.

Cathleen clasped round her neck her one good piece of
jewellery, an antique peridot pendant which Jonathon had
given to her after Debby's birth. She wasn't wearing it
because of its associations, but for the simple practical
reason that she had nothing else. The stone made her eyes
look very green. She felt as if she could have been beautiful
tonight, if only – what? If the setting, the circumstances,
the man, were right?

And they were all wrong, so that her eyes shone for
nothing. The party was not for her. In some mysterious
way it was for Kitty.

Which reminded her that she ought to see if Kitty had
successfully managed the borrowed dress.

There was no answer when she tapped at Kitty's door.
She had to go in without permission. She found Kitty sitting
in her dressing-gown on the side of the bed holding the
ruby necklace.

When Cathleen came in she started violently. Her eyes
flew to the door with a look of terror. At once she tried to
disguise her feelings by saying rapidly,

'I don't feel well. I think I'm getting one of my migraines.'

'Kitty, you can't be! You'll have to come down.'

'You don't know what my headaches are like.'

'Then take some aspirin. My head has been aching ever
since yesterday, too.'

195

At that, Kitty's face went wooden. She fiddled with the necklace, muttering that she didn't know why she should have to do something she hated, it wasn't her party, it was Aunt Tilly's, and Aunt Tilly had never had to try to dance with one leg shorter than the other.

'Kitty, for goodness' sake don't be such a baby!' Cathleen exclaimed exasperatedly. 'You've got a pretty face and beautiful hair. You're lucky enough to live in a castle and to have a fabulous necklace to wear. Any other girl with those assets would make herself irresistible. There's no reason why you can't. So come along. Get out of that dressing-gown. I'll do your hair and your make-up for you, if you'll let me.'

'Why should you bother?' Kitty said sulkily.

'Goodness knows why I should bother, but if your aunt feels like some gaiety after the gloom we've been living in lately, I think it's up to us to support her.'

'You're very sure of yourself, Mrs. Lamb.'

'Call me Cathleen, couldn't you? After all, you're going to wear my dress.'

Kitty stood up and let her dressing-gown slide to the floor. Her body was bony and childish. Cathleen had fears that even with the taking in she and Peggy, who had proved an expert needlewoman, had done, the dress would still be too big.

'Really, I believe you've lost weight since lunch time. Hold your shoulders up, darling. Push out your breasts. That's better. You know, it mightn't be too late even now to have an operation on that hip. It would be worth finding out about, wouldn't it?'

Kitty whispered, 'I'm frightened.'

'Of an operation?'

'No. Not of that.'

'Then of what?'

A brief silence hung between them. Cathleen waited, not

breathing. But Kitty had mastered her impulse to confide. She turned away, saying, 'I don't know why you're doing this for me.'

Cathleen picked up the dress wearily.

'Nor do I. But I'm tired of asking questions. And of answering them. Why don't we pretend we've just met? We're getting ready for a party, and we're late. Turn round while I fasten you. I believe the dress fits very well after all. You have pretty shoulders. Now the necklace. Wouldn't it be a nice idea if you went up and let your mother see you.'

'With this?' Kitty touched the gleaming red stones. They looked like blood against her transparent skin.

'She'd like to see you wearing it.'

'It's supposed to be always for the eldest son's wife. Grandmother and great-grandmother left Aunt Tilly several good pieces, but this and a diamond ring and earrings became my mother's when she married my father. They're not to be sold any more than any of the land is. It seems silly, being poor when we have assets like this. It's a kind of ridiculous family pride, just like Aunt Tilly feeling she has to give these parties to show people we're still alive.'

'Then your aunt must have hated selling the Fabergé brooch.'

'I don't know anything about that.' Kitty turned away, but not before Cathleen had seen the fear leap into her eyes.

'Should the necklace have been for Shamus's wife?' Cathleen persisted. She wondered if Kitty knew that Moira was dead. 'And then Rory's, now that Shamus is dead. And Liam's if Rory never married. Liam comes last,' she added reflectively.

'It isn't fair, being a third brother,' Kitty burst out. 'One is always at the bottom. Poor Liam only has his horses.'

'What would Rory have had if Shamus hadn't died?'

'But he did. Didn't he?'

Cathleen bit her lip. She had said she wouldn't ask any more questions. The crows' wings were flapping again.

'Grab the necklace while you can,' she said brusquely. 'It's beautiful. It makes you look rich and important and cherished.'

'Cher—' Kitty's lip trembled. She bent her head. 'All right,' she said in a low voice. 'I will go up and see mother.'

It was time to go downstairs. Several cars had arrived, and Rory and Magdalene could no longer be drinking alone.

Cathleen paused on the stairs, overcome by an enormous reluctance. Her feeling that something was going to happen was overwhelming.

Peggy Moloney came to hang over the banisters beside her. She looked lonely and wistful in her nurse's uniform, too young and lively to be shut out from a party.

'You look nice, Mrs. Lamb. It's a grand party, isn't it? I saw Magdalene Driscoll come. She looked wonderful. Even Kitty – you know something. When her mother saw her she began to cry. Truly. She had real tears in her eyes. I almost cried, too. It was so touching, she seemed so happy to see her daughter dressed the way she should be. Or maybe because she was wearing the rubies. You know, Miss O'Riordan has hidden them in the funniest place. In a hatbox in the top of the wardrobe.'

'How do you know?'

'Because she came in one night not long ago and said she was nervous about jewellery like that being locked in a jewel box. It was the obvious place for a burglar to look. She was going to take charge of them herself, she said. But I never did see where she put them until she got them out today. Would you believe it? In that hatbox among all the osprey feathers! Wouldn't anyone else keep things like that in a bank?'

Peggy giggled. 'You know, this place gets me down, but in another way it's fascinating, isn't it? Don't you feel that? It's like nowhere else in the world.'

'I know what you mean,' Cathleen agreed.

'Last night I was scared,' Peggy confessed. 'Miss O'Riordan sat there like a broomstick, never taking her eyes off my patient, and I had the funniest feeling that if my patient ever really began to talk she'd – well, something would happen to her. She'd have to be kept quiet, do you know what I mean? But then today it was different again, everyone excited about a party as if there'd never been anything odd happening. I must have been imagining things from not getting enough sleep.'

'Did your patient say anything?'

'Only that "lie" thing. I think it's Liam she wants. He was supposed to have been her favourite.'

Peggy was looking at Cathleen again admiringly.

'I must say you've recovered since this morning. You look bonny now.'

'I'm all right. My head only aches a little. They must have stuffed me with sedatives to make me so helpless yesterday. It all seems like a dream now.'

'Were you really pushed down the stairs?' Peggy asked fearfully.

There was a party and a truce. She had promised Rory.

'I don't know. It all does seem like a dream. Like the things you imagined about Miss O'Riordan in the night.'

'I know,' said Peggy solemnly. 'After all, nothing has happened, has it, except that drunk tinker falling in the pool, poor fellow.'

Someone was singing softly, crossing the hall.

'And it will not be long now,
Till our wedding day . . .'

The dark heads were so alike. But this one was Rory's. He had a glass in his hand. He had been drinking with Magdalene. Magdalene who insisted he was in love with someone else ...

He looked up, his eyes sparkling.

'Aren't you coming down, Cathleen? You're the last.'

She came slowly, her face contained.

'Colonel Green's been asking for you. The young English woman with the beautiful eyes, he said. The blind old fool!'

'Blind?'

Rory grinned.

'Sure, and he said your eyes were blue. We nearly had a fight.'

'Fool yourself! You've been drinking.'

'And so will you be, before the night's over, my honey.'

Cathleen hesitated, wanting suddenly to run away.

'Rory, what *is* this all about?'

'You're an onlooker, remember. But you'll need a drink.' For the merest second the grimness showed beneath his deliberate gaiety. Then he said, 'It seems to be Kitty's coming-out party, long overdue. Perhaps it's an ill-wind after all. Kitty looks fine. You're a clever girl, Cathleen. and a kind one. But, my God, if all the English had been like you there'd never have been a war, and what would the brave O'Riordans have done then?'

'You're crazy.'

'Come and fill Kitty up with champagne. The rest of us don't need encouragement.'

'Is it – important to do that?'

'It's important.'

The dream had come back. They were all in the drawing-room, the well-dressed, noisy, laughing, people. Colonel Green saw Cathleen and Rory come in, and came forward, staring intently.

'By George, Rory, you're right. How could I have made such a mistake? My sight must be failing. Never made such a mistake in my life before. Pride myself on my powers of observation. But one thing we were both right about. They're magnificent.'

'Whatever are you talking about, Colonel?' Cathleen asked.

'Your eyes, m'dear. Can't think how I thought they were blue.'

Rory had pushed a glass of champagne into her hand and gone.

'Unexpected pleasure, this. Like old times. Matilda was a great hand at the spontaneous party. Drinks at the Castle, she'd say, and we'd all come. Poor Cecilia's illness has cast a shadow over the last couple of years, of course. But damn it, one can't go round on tiptoe forever.'

Liam was beside Cathleen, refilling her glass. His eyes had their blazing, blue, frenetic look of excitement.

'Rory neglecting you?' he said casually.

'Liam, I believe you're jealous!'

He nodded. He looked startlingly handsome.

'I'm jealous of everyone who talks to you, not only Rory. I'm a very possessive person, did you know? Anyway, Rory's been drinking with Magdalene for the last hour. But I wouldn't want you hurt by him.'

'I won't be hurt. I've only been interested in finding out about Eileen Burke. That's why I went with him this morning.'

'Don't let yourself get taken for a ride.'

'What do you mean?'

'This is a party. No shop talk. I won't even use the opportunity to defend myself. A slander for a slander, so to speak. Kitty looks very grand, doesn't she?'

It was true. Now that she was the centre of attention, Kitty must have found that the becoming dress and the jewels gave her confidence, for she was more animated than

Cathleen had ever seen her. She was talking to a fair-haired man who obviously found her large innocent eyes very attractive. He was listening with close attention.

'Aunt Tilly was right, after all,' said Liam.

'About Kitty having the necklace?'

'Yes. Why shouldn't she? Apart from anything else, it will stop Magdalene from marrying Rory for it.'

'Are you telling me that's why she wanted to marry Shamus?'

'How would I know? She's a calculating bi— Sorry But look at that sharp nose.'

Magdalene had her hair piled high on her head and covered with a light gauzy scarf. She looked elegant and overbred and above the useless habit of telling lies.

'I like her,' Cathleen said briefly.

'Do you? Sorry.' Liam smiled charmingly. 'I must sound like a jealous old woman. I automatically take against what my brothers like. It's a bad habit I have. By the way, I was serious about us meeting in London later on. Kitty, too, if she'll come. Between us, I'm sure we could turn her into a perfectly normal and happy person.'

'She's doing that now, without our help,' Cathleen pointed out.

'Oh, she's had some champagne.'

'No. She's had the assurance that she counts for a little. Both from her mother and her aunt. It's rather late, but perhaps not too late.'

Liam was frowning.

'What do you mean?'

'I was just wondering if it were really her aunt who had dominated her— Oh, nothing. Just a fancy. But she might be a little hard to pry loose from the rubies now she's worn them.'

She hadn't the least idea why she had said that. She had just become aware of Liam's sharp, suspicious look when

Miss O'Riordan, in black velvet with a drunkenly floating stole of ostrich feathers, that made her look more than ever like an elongated and slightly seedy crow, came swooping down on them.

'Mrs. Lamb! I want you to meet my old friend, Lord Laver. He's just been having a wildly dissolute time doing the London night-clubs. I don't think Mrs. Lamb is an authority on night-clubs, Jeremy. It wasn't one of her references when I employed her.' Miss O'Riordan gave her hoarse laugh. She had on too much rouge, and her thin lips were painted dark red, as were her fingernails. Her eyes glittered beneath green-smeared lids. Oddly enough, she looked neither pathetic nor comic, but sheerly magnificent.

She had developed one idiosyncracy, however, that was disturbing. She kept glancing at the windows and saying 'How dark is it? No, no lights yet, Liam, please. The dusk is kinder to us. And why is your glass empty, dear boy? Fill it up. There aren't any pools around here to tumble in. No one, without God's help, could drown in the lily pond. Ah, Colonel! Colonel, do you remember that ball we had when Patrick was still alive? We strung lights in the trees, had an orchestra from Dublin.'

'Indeed, I remember. There was Patrick, Paddy O'Connal, Dermot Donovan, Michael O'Neill. All gone now, may their souls rest in peace. That was before your time, Liam. Or was it, Matilda? Was Liam born then, or did Cecilia just have the two?'

'Liam was born later. Oh, he may have been thought of then, how would I be knowing? Excuse me, Colonel. Mary Kate seems to want something.'

Because she could never do anything inconspicuously, Miss O'Riordan's passage across the room to the door was watched by everybody.

It was then that the tension caught Cathleen again. She

didn't hear what the elderly immaculate and well-preserved Lord Laver was saying. She stared at Mary Kate's plump figure in the doorway. It somehow communicated distress.

Her words to Miss O'Riordan were inaudible, but Aunt Tilly had no such discretion. She turned and called in her harsh penetrating voice,

'Liam! Mary Kate says there's a young woman asking to see you. She's put her in the billiard room.'

Liam's face went still.

'Who?'

A glass clinked. Then the room was utterly quiet. It was one of those dramatic moments as in a theatre, Cathleen thought, when the audience was caught in the unendurable suspense of the play. Everyone waited for the woman to be named. Eileen Burke?

Aunt Tilly lifted her raddled proud old face.

'She says her name is Moira, and that she's your wife.'

CHAPTER NINETEEN

EVERYONE was aware of the strange duel between the two of them, the tall old woman in black, with her high-held head, and Liam, staring at her with eyes that were the colour of the water in the Connemara lakes on a sunny day. His face was incredulous, angry, baffled – and frightened.

'This is a trick,' he said in a low voice. He seemed unaware of anyone in the room except his aunt. Somehow this was private between the two of them.

'Then you'd better prove it, hadn't you?' Miss O'Riordan's voice was level and emotionless. 'But if you were being married, dear boy, it would have been courtesy to tell your family.'

Liam gave a stifled exclamation. He pushed people aside and strode towards the door.

'Where's Mary Kate? She's playing a trick on me.'

'Mary Kate has merely had the sense not to leave a young woman standing at the door. Go and see her, Liam, for goodness sake. You're spoiling my party.' Miss O'Riordan's face was as emotionless as her voice, a mask, with eyes narrowed to expressionless slits. 'She has a pretty name, though. Moira. I think we should all meet her, since Liam seems so reluctant. Who's coming? Rory? Kitty?'

Liam had gone swiftly ahead down the passage to the billiard room. Cathleen felt someone take her arm. It was Rory.

'You'd better come, too.' His voice was as expressionless as his aunt's had been.

It was almost dark in the passage, but in the long billiard room with the heavy curtains draped back from the windows there was the shadowy soft light of evening.

The girl sat at the other end of the room with her face half-turned to the door. She was very slight. Her red hair, luxuriant and shining, hung loose over her shoulders, half hiding her face. She drooped a little, as if she were tired. Indeed, she had seemed to be half-dozing in the dusk, for she didn't start up until Liam exclaimed in a hoarse incredibly shocked voice,

'*Moira!* They told me you were dead! They tricked me!'

The red hair was flung back, the pale face lifted.

'Put on the lights, Liam,' said Magdalene Driscoll. 'Let's see who's been tricked.'

Rory reached out and turned on the light switch. His fingers were biting into Cathleen's arm, hurting badly. She found the pain curiously welcome. It made Liam's outraged and frightened face almost bearable.

Almost bearable, too, the look of sad and hopeless confirmation in Aunt Tilly's.

'So it worked, Liam' she said flatly. 'Yes, it was my scheme. I had to be sure.'

'Sure of what, for heavens' sake?' Liam shouted. 'That I once knew a girl called Moira? She wouldn't be the first who's wanted to marry me or even lied that she did. If this is a joke, Aunt Tilly, your sense of humour is appalling.'

'It isn't a joke, Liam. It's my apology – my public apology – to Shamus. Now, if our guests will excuse you, I'm afraid there are a couple of policemen waiting to see you. They seem to have located a woman called Eileen Burke in Athlone. She has some rather disturbing accusations to make against you, including assault and kidnapping.'

'Kidnapping! What utter nonsense! Kitty and I merely looked after her baby while she wasn't able to. She'd fallen and hurt her leg. Kitty! Isn't that true?'

Kitty put her face in her hands and began to weep, her childishly narrow shoulders shaking.

'I didn't know!' she sobbed. 'I didn't know!'

'This woman claims you took the baby and said it would only be returned unharmed if she agreed to what you suggested. You apparently trusted her too much. But don't we all make that mistake some time? Fight that out with the police, boy. I'm too old, too tired. Sweet heaven, I'm tired.'

Liam looked from left to right. The room, Cathleen thought, must have seemed to him full of accusing faces. His own face suddenly looked narrow and cunning, as it must have looked when he had stood over Eileen Burke, threatening her with harm to her child.

'Look out!' cried Colonel Green in the background.

But it was too late. Liam had backed swiftly to one of the long windows, flung it open, and leaped out.

Two of the men went to follow him, but Rory called sharply, 'Let him go'.

'Let him go!' repeated Colonel Green in amazement. 'If I get this right, that bastard – and I don't apologize for the word – married this girl we've all been made to understand was Shamus's wife, and completely tricked the poor thing.'

'Under Shamus's name,' said Magdalene bitterly. 'In a shoddy little ceremony at the Register office. And nobody knew, not even Shamus until that night when he saw Moira leaving the castle and somehow wrested the truth out of Liam. I'm not saying his death wasn't an accident. But I do know he fell and cracked his head on that desk as the result of a blow from his charming youngest brother. And that his mother most likely came in and saw Liam leaving. What has she been trying to say lately but Liam, Liam's living a lie! Pretty, isn't it?' She bent her head. 'Now I've had my revenge. If you all want to know, I hated it. Hated it. But my dear Shamus can now rest in peace.' Her voice shook. 'Thank you, Miss O'Riordan. That was – very great – of you.'

She went out, trying with shaking fingers to pin up her hair. Kitty, although the tears were still shining on her cheeks, surprisingly enough had grown quite calm. She went across to Miss O'Riordan and put her arm round the stiffly erect figure.

'Come, Aunt Tilly. Let's go upstairs. I'll get you a drink.'

'Yes,' said Miss O'Riordan quite strongly. 'I need a drink. Faugh! Not that insipid champagne. Whisky, it is. And none of your delicate touch.'

Colonel Green sniffed loudly.

'Remarkable woman,' he muttered. 'Remarkable. Well, well! What's to be done about your brother, Rory?'

'Leave him,' said Rory curtly. 'He'll have gone to the stables. That's where he always went when he sulked as a boy. Shamus and I – perhaps we were to blame. How does one know?'

Cathleen curled her fingers in his. She felt his painful answering grip.

'It had to be done,' he said, as if speaking to himself.

'Was he always a jealous fellow?' Colonel Green asked.

'Always. He seemed to have been born that way. Hated being the youngest brother. He compensated himself with dreams of grandeur, such as breeding famous horses, winning great races, becoming a personality in that world. Marrying a humble person like Moira Regan didn't fit into the picture at all. But she was a good girl, and marriage was the only way he could get her. That's another characteristic of my brother, what he wants he goes to any lengths to get. Anyway, he lied to her from start to finish. He took rooms in Dublin and lived with her there whenever it suited him. He told her he was away a great deal on a travelling job. Moira must have been a dreamy and gullible person, perhaps even a little simple. She didn't doubt his word at first. But later, by some means, she found out who he was – or who he had said he was – Shamus O'Riordan of Loughneath Castle. So naturally, feeling a little indignant about the two rooms in Dublin, she came here to find out the truth of the matter.'

'Good lord! And no one saw her but Mary Kate?'

'Mary Kate left her in the billiard room, just as she did Magdalene tonight. She intended to tell Shamus when he came in that someone was waiting for him, but Liam came in first, luckily for him. Somehow, I don't know how, except that Moira must have been an obedient person, he persuaded her to go back to Dublin. He'd make the announcement about their marriage, when he'd paved the way with his mother and so on. Moira doesn't seem to have been an acquisitive girl. And God help her, she loved him and was ready to forgive him anything. She still thought he was Shamus, of course. But the next day she saw the shocking news of Shamus's death in the paper.'

'And she thought it was her husband!' Cathleen exclaimed.

'She did. And she decided, with her quite outstanding pride and decency, that if the O'Riordans wanted nothing of her, she wanted nothing of them. She was too good for us, if the truth be known. Anyway, she packed her stuff and went off to London to start again. That's why we found no trace of her when we looked for her. Liam, if you can believe it, helped us search.'

'And then?' Colonel Green asked.

'Three years later Moira came back on a visit to Dublin at the time of the Dublin Horse Show and there, staring at her from the newspaper, was a picture of my good-looking younger brother, Mr. Liam O'Riordan, winning one of the main jumping events. Her husband. Not Shamus, but Liam.'

'Extraordinary!' muttered the Colonel.

'Not more extraordinary than my sister-in-law. She might have been easily fooled, but she was all the things no one believes in much nowadays, idealistic, loyal, loving, true.

The only action she took was to tell her two brothers the terrible thing that had happened to her, and while they were planning not only how she, but they too could cash in on such a windfall, she quietly drowned herself. She had loved Liam too much. She had had her heart broken.'

Cathleen's fingers moved in his. He looked down at her.

'Do you never have melodramas like this in your country? The O'Riordans indulge in them constantly. As you'll discover, my darling.'

Colonel Green har-rumphed with delicacy.

'You two have something to say to one another. I think the rest of us could well follow Matilda's example and go and find another drink. Remarkable business, this. Remarkable! But I must say I never thought Shamus . . .'

His voice died away as the other guests discreetly followed his example. A loud knock came at the door and Sergeant O'Grady put his head in.

'Sorry to interrupt you, sir. Been waiting for Mr. Liam O'Riordan. There's a question or two I want to put to him.'

'You'll find him down at the stables.'

'The stables?'

'Yes. He won't put up a fight, sergeant. I know him. He always runs away.'

'Thank you, sir.'

'Like leaving your mother and Shamus that night,' said Cathleen. 'How could he bear to?'

'He didn't dare to be seen in the room. He had to leave them to be found by someone else.'

'But your aunt has known about this?'

'Since Moira reappeared, yes. Liam confided in her, and she's been protecting him. She's been afraid poor mother would get her speech back and tell the truth. It must have been a nightmare for her, the gallant old thing.'

'Gallant?'

'Yes. The word's the right one. And she'd have gone on protecting Liam if he hadn't committed the ultimate offence, the unforgiveable one. He decided to cash in on Danny Regan's game and go one better.'

Cathleen lifted a horrified face.

'You mean, he deliberately invented the story that he and Moira had had a child?'

'Exactly. He knew Aunt Tilly would go to any lengths to stop his name being blackened, with the scandal of his wife's suicide. Indeed, to stop a possible prosecution for murder. Who knows how Shamus really died that night? And Liam couldn't have his life blighted by a false marriage and an illegitimate child. The child was a brilliant stroke of imagination. The story was that it had been born in England, and Liam himself hadn't known about it until recently.'

Rory's eyes were dark with disillusion.

'I'm afraid my brother thought Aunt Tilly loved him enough to even sell the family jewels for him. He planned that if he got sufficient money he'd go to England and start breeding horses in a big way. He was always completely impractical. Had his head full of dreams, and filled Kitty's with them, too. Poor little Kitty was his sycophant.'

'Rory, how did you find out all this?'

'I'd found out quite a lot from Moira's brother in Dublin yesterday. I told you that. He, by the way, was the fellow who was lurking outside your hotel that night. The word had got around that you were collecting money. The crows were gathering. And they didn't trust Liam. But the rest I got from Eileen Burke this afternoon.'

'You found her!'

'I wasn't idle while you were so kindly dressing Kitty for her ball.'

'How did you find Eileen Burke?'

'Luck. A little deduction. I knew Liam wouldn't risk her being in Galway. Athlone was the next big town.

I guessed she had some injury, and of course, the baby boy. I simply went round the hotels. I might say she was so scared when I walked in, she must have thought I intended to take her baby, too.'

'Liam did that? He hid the baby in the west wing?'

'Yes, with Kitty's help, and a little of my mother's sedatives. They kept the boy asleep all the time.'

'So it really was Kitty who pushed me down the stairs, and who frightened Macushla that day. She must have an intense loyalty for Liam.'

'She has. She loved him and clung to him too much. I gather she overheard a telephone conversation that made her suspicious and frightened.'

'And knew that I'd heard it, too,' said Cathleen. 'So I had to be watched. Made to go away, or even been got rid of. I think she must be a bit unbalanced where Liam is concerned. She would do anything to protect him, wouldn't she?'

'I believe so. She is such a solitary. Aunt Tilly's fault, mother's, the fault of all of us.'

'Poor Kitty,' said Cathleen sadly. 'But let's keep her out of this, if we can. Did Eileen Burke tell you everything?'

'Everything. Even to blaming herself for persuading her weak husband into this. She's an unpleasant woman, mercenary, vain, ambitious. She suspected Liam wasn't playing fair, so she decided that she would deliberately – subtly, of course – spread the rumour about the child which hitherto only Aunt Tilly had known. She thought it would give the Regans a strong hold over Liam. You see the nasty little circle it was, the one biting the other. Liam was furious, of course, and that was how he and Danny came to have the argument at their rendezvous at the pool. There's no doubt Danny was helped to his death. Liam couldn't trust him any more. He had to keep him and his wife quiet until the last coup.'

'Which meant getting all the jewels?'

'Yes. Their loss wouldn't have been discovered until my mother died, and then we'd be expected to assume that Aunt Tilly had sold them to pay her gambling debts. She has always been a reckless gambler. No doubt Liam thought the jewels were his legitimate share of the family fortune. At least, they were all that could be turned into cash, with Aunt Tilly's co-operation. So that was the ultimatum in the last blackmailing letter to her. It told her not to laugh at anybody's funeral because the wrong person was dead.'

'So then she must have known it was Liam, and she hid the ruby necklace in the hatbox for safety. But why did she still keep silent?'

'I don't know. Perhaps she wanted retribution on a grand scale. That's her nature. You heard her say she wanted to make a public apology to Shamus, for hiding the truth for so long. So finally she hit on the plan to startle Liam into giving himself away by getting Magdalene to act Moira. That's why the light had to be just right, neither too dark nor too light. Aunt Tilly took me into her confidence this afternoon and we rehearsed Magdalene and Mary Kate. That's how it happened.'

He moved tiredly. 'But I think we should go and find Aunt Tilly.'

There were lights everywhere now. The castle looked as if it were lit for genuine festivities, not for a party that had come to an abrupt end, with the guests tactfully leaving.

Magdalene was coming down the stairs, her hair hidden by the filmy green scarf.

When Rory put out his hands to her she made a quick gesture, moving away.

'Just let me go, Rory. Oh, I'll come back to your next party. But this one's over. Finished.'

Her eyes were full of tears.

'I never did stop loving Shamus, you know. But I can

think about him easily now. Good night, you two. If you're looking for Kitty, she's up with her mother, holding her hand. Aunt Tilly seems to have disappeared, the old monster.' There was wry affection in Magdalene's voice. 'Don't let her have sung her swansong. The castle wouldn't be the same without her.'

The big bedroom with the shadowy four-poster was empty. Upstairs Kitty sat on the floor with her head resting on the side of her mother's bed, while in the background Peggy made violent signs not to disturb them.

'They're both asleep,' she hissed.

Perhaps somewhere Miss O'Riordan was asleep, too, like Kitty, overcome with the exhaustion of sleepless nights, worry, fear, skipped meals, and finally the end of an illusion.

Rory was getting anxious.

'She won't be asleep. Have you ever seen her sleeping? Personally, I don't believe she ever closes her eyes. When I was small I used to think she was like a very thin old Buddha sitting with her hands clasped, and watching everything!'

He was talking to allay Cathleen's fear.

'She couldn't even have been very old then. She's always seemed everlasting to me. She was a far greater personality in our childhood than mother ever was. I think mother was always terrified of her, and of my father, too. She was too gentle for a family like ours.'

'Rory, do you think she's gone out looking for Liam?'

'No.'

'But she cared so much for him—'

'Aunt Tilly loves or hates. Something you'll discover for yourself. She won't be looking for Liam now. When she made her decision this morning, that was the end.'

'Then I know where she'll be!' Cathleen cried. 'She was there the night of the thunderstorm. In the room where she keeps her old clothes. Her museum.'

And there, surely enough, she sat, a stiff figure on the upright chair, a cross between the Buddha Rory had talked of and a fashionable young woman of the late nineteen twenties, dressed in a sequin-trimmed ball dress. Her hands were quietly folded in her lap, her face and neck grotesquely wrinkled above the youthful dress. Her narrowed eyes, turned to Rory and Cathleen, had a stubborn crafty look.

'If you've come to persuade me to go downstairs, you're wasting your time,' she said. 'I'll not be at that ball.'

'Everyone's gone home,' Cathleen said gently. 'And you must come to bed.'

'Ha! Those words have a familiar sound. Come to bed, he says. Come to bed, Tilly. You look damned fine in that dress, he says. You're a fine woman, Tilly O'Riordan. Ah sure, there's time to talk of wedding rings later. Have some more champagne, my darling! Come to bed . . .'

She was twisting something in her long bony fingers.

'We could hear the violins,' she said. 'They were playing the old Irish songs. *And it will not be long now . . .*' her voice was thin and hoarse and absurdly off key, '*till our wedding day . . .*'

With matter-of-fact vigour she tore the paper in her hands to pieces.

'Michael O'Neill, the black-hearted traitor,' she said grimly. 'And down there in the dark at this minute his son is running away. Like his father ran away. All these years I've given him all that misguided love. I might have known he'd be his father over again. I took a long time to be convinced there wasn't something to save. I didn't mind him getting in a mess over a girl. That's human enough. And I wouldn't believe there was anything sinister about that wretched man's drowning. A lucky accident, I thought. But then there was the business of the Brady child not being who I'd been told he was. And that morbid discovery of Mrs. Lamb's. The baby's shoe. One has to face facts

215

some time. One doesn't back a horse with a faulty heart. One destroys it . . .'

She looked up with her keen raking gaze.

'Well, you two! What are you staring at? If you must know, I put on this dress and sat here pretending to myself that that ball had never started, that Michael O'Neill had never set foot in this house, that—' Her lips began to tremble uncontrollably, 'Damn you, stop staring! If you must know, it was worth it. Heaven help me, I'd do it again. Even to that grisly four months in Brighton in the company of your saintly mother who was having a cuckoo foisted on her.'

She glared at Cathleen and Rory.

'I've told you nothing, do you hear? Nothing.'

She got to her feet. Just for one moment her aggressive mask cracked and the agony showed through. Then she said briskly,

'Now we must make amends. Kitty keeps the rubies. Do you hear, Mrs. Lamb?'

'What's it to do with me?' Cathleen asked.

'It's no more to do with you than any of the other things you've resolutely made your business since you came here. But although I'm old and eccentric and a little drunk and perhaps mad, I'm not blind. Now leave me.'

CHAPTER TWENTY

THE fantastic evening was not yet over. Patsy had come stumbling in the front door crying in a broken-hearted voice, 'That big brute of a stallion has come back saddled and riderless. Mr. Liam should never have been riding him in the dark. I've said over and over that beast weren't to be trusted.'

Rory's face went still.

'Where are the police?'

'They've taken torches. Young Jim's gone, too. I'd be thinking he'd be down at the jumps. Are you coming, sir?'

'Stay here,' Rory said to Cathleen, and was gone.

So she had to sit with only a tear-smeared swollen-eyed Mary Kate for company, and think of the magnificent ruthless old woman upstairs tearing up the letter Cathleen herself had unearthed in her research – *You must have been bewitched or under the influence of Patsy's poteen. I deny every word* . . . – and having the courage to bring her greatly-loved son for whom she had lied, stolen, and almost wrecked Kitty's life, to justice. Perhaps Liam had been the victim of the circumstances of his birth, perhaps he had inherited his father's weaknesses, or too much of his mother's arrogance and ruthlessness without her leavening of humour and courage. Certainly his mother had secretly spoilt him outrageously, encouraging him to think that he would be denied nothing and forgiven everything. Miss O'Riordan's loves were violent and loyal and all-embracing until the turning point came. Liam had shown a diabolical cleverness in knowing he could exploit his mother's vulnerability and guilt about a child born secretly and irregularly. His stupidity had lain in not recognizing that there could be a breaking-point in her loyalty.

Perhaps at the end Cathleen herself had been responsible for his downfall. She guessed he had begun to want her as badly as he had wanted Moira Regan, but he had had the sense to know she couldn't be had so simply. So he had had to strut and show off, to boast of his ambitions, most of all to acquire money. And cope with the complication of Kitty's jealous love for a brother who was not a brother . . .

At midnight they brought in the hurdle bearing the broken body . . .

The conversation in Miss O'Riordan's museum might not have taken place. It was never referred to again. A week later Miss O'Riordan sent for Cathleen.

Cathleen found her sitting up in bed, the sable cape askew over her shoulders, her face sharp and alert. Kitty stood at the window, her back turned.

'Well, Mrs. Lamb. Now you've been here long enough to discover the sort of people we are, are you prepared to stay?'

The week had been sad and confusing, and very lonely. Cathleen had seen little of Miss O'Riordan or of Kitty with her red-rimmed eyes, even less of Rory. She had kept out of the way, working in the library, but feeling useless and forgotten.

'But of course, Miss O'Riordan. We've scarcely begun our work. As soon as you feel fit enough—'

'We're not talking about my state of mind,' Miss O'Riordan interrupted brusquely, 'but yours. As I understand it, a book can only be a success if its author feels personally involved. Do you now regard yourself as sufficiently identified with us?'

It was as if all the melodrama and tragedy had been laid on as a testing process for her! An ordeal by fire, to prove

her a worthy historian of this crazy family. Cathleen meant
to say that she felt more than a little involved. Instead she
answered simply,

'I feel alive again.'

Miss O'Riordan regarded her with interest.

'Now I begin to see what was lacking in your appearance
when I first interviewed you. Then I thought you were
another Cecilia. Now I can see you're not.' There was a
certain satisfaction in her voice. 'Definitely not.'

Presently she added, 'Mere good looks aren't enough.
It's the spirit inside the flesh that makes beauty. I believe
that strange creature, Moira, had it. Mary Kate says so.
Liam was luckier than he knew.'

She spoke quietly and without bitterness. Her own fiery
and undefeated spirit lay very close beneath the finely-drawn
flesh.

But in a moment her eyes were snapping vigorously.

'Then here's my plan, Mrs. Lamb. Tomorrow you'll
drive Kitty and me to Dublin. I want to see Sister Mary
Martha who may need a little reassuring after that perplexing
affair with the Brady child. Besides, I'd like to see the little
ones again. While I do that, you are to take Kitty shopping.
Rory has stopped behaving like an unpopular Government
and handed me back my five hundred pounds, together
with a little extra. As long as there's something left so that
I can follow a horse or two, you may spend the major part
of it on a good wardrobe for Kitty. She's to start leading a
much more active life. See that there's a good ball dress, and
some snappy little cocktail affairs.'

Kitty spun round.

'Aunt Tilly, I won't be treated like a schoolgirl. I can
buy my own clothes.'

Aunt Tilly gave her hoarse chuckle.

'Splendid, child, splendid! I detected a flash of O'Riordan
spirit there, thank God.' Her voice hardened. 'But on this

occasion you'll do as I say. Mrs. Lamb isn't patronizing you. She's shown already that she can be your friend, and little enough you deserve that.'

Kitty flushed, but stubbornly kept her head high.

'I'm not sorry for anything.' In a low voice she added, 'I'd have died for Liam.'

'And now you'll live for me. We're a diminished family, and we must stick together. And by the way, get some riding clothes. I want you to learn to ride.'

'Aunt Tilly!' Kitty spoke in a shocked whisper. 'You're not trying to make me take Liam's place!'

Aunt Tilly sat upright, her eyes blazing.

'How dare you! What a thing to say!'

Her flat chest heaved. She had difficulty in controlling her emotion. At last she said dryly, tiredly,

'No, I'm not trying to make you take your brother's place. I'm merely trying to make sure that you find a husband.'

Dublin was grey beneath a grey sky. The ragged jaunty beggar was playing his accordion on the humped bridge over the Liffey. Gulls drifted in slanting flight. A red-headed girl wandered dreamily by, swinging her shopping bag. A cat washed itself in the doorway of a shop spilling over with secondhand books and grime-obscured paintings. With a lively jingling, a cart drawn by a leisurely donkey, and full of straggle-haired bright-eyed children, threaded its way among the traffic. Someone was whistling. *There's a colleen fair as may, for a year and for a day . . .*

Cathleen looked round with swift apprehension. A workman, carrying a crate into a warehouse, stopped whistling and winked impudently.

Her heart quickened. There were no crows here. They had all flown away.

But a hand was laid on her arm, holding her back.

'What have you done with Kitty?' Rory asked.

'What are you doing here? Following me?' She had almost not been able to keep the joy out of her voice.

'Sure, I've been following you.'

'Then you know I left Kitty at the hotel. She was tired. We've shopped all day. Successfully, too. You'd be surprised at how animated Kitty got. But now she wants to rest, and I—'

'Yes? What about you?'

'Did you follow me particularly?'

'I did. I wanted to talk to you away from the castle, clear of all that mess. Do you understand?'

'I think so.'

'Cathleen!' Again his hard grip was hurting her. 'You've been haunted by your child. What about your husband?'

Jonathon – she remembered how he had sometimes withdrawn his hand when she had held it too eagerly, too publicly. She knew what it was now – he had been a perfectly good man who had somehow diminished her spirit.

Rory would hold her in public, bruising her if he wanted to, proclaiming to the world his possession. He would hurt her and make her blazingly angry, and she would never for a moment not know what it was to be alive. Their children would have brilliant black eyes and smiles that broke one's heart.

'Jonathon's gone, Rory,' she said soberly. 'No more ghosts.'

'Then we'd better be getting home.' Only his hurting grip betrayed his feelings. 'Hadn't we?'

The pain stung her to retaliate.

'Yes, and I'll tell you this, Rory O'Riordan. Magdalene said you were in love with someone else, but if you dare to be – if you dare—'

He spoke in his charming deliberate brogue.

'You've got a quick tongue in your head, to be sure.

If you'll not be keeping a check on it I'll take the pins out of your hair and let it tumble down. That would be a foine sight in O'Connell Street. A very foine sight,' he said in his caressing voice.

It was impossible to think that his eyes had ever been hard or insolent or angry, as they dwelt now on thoughts of her spilt hair.

DOROTHY EDEN

Never Call It Loving

The Story of the magnificent love affair that scandalised 19th Century England.

From the moment they met, Charles Parnell, the famous Irish patriot, and Kitty O'Shea, the wife of his colleague, were swept forward in a passionate sense of adventure. She was beautiful and young, he was a man of affairs with 'Home Rule' as his watchword. But from friendship and mutual admiration they were thrown into a turbulent, overpowering love that brought them public scorn and private grief, and the last separation from which there is no turning back.

'A certain winner'

Daily Mirror

'Dorothy Eden brings the period vividly to life and gives dignity and pathos to the ill-fated lover'

Woman's Journal

CORONET BOOKS

OTHER NOVELS BY DOROTHY EDEN
FROM CORONET

All these books are available at your local bookshop or newsagent, or can be ordered direct from the publisher. Just tick the titles you want and fill in the form below.

Prices and availability subject to change without notice.

CORONET BOOKS, P.O. Box 11, Falmouth, Cornwall.

Please send cheque or postal order, and allow the following for postage and packing:

U.K. – One book 18p plus 8p per copy for each additional book ordered, up to a maximum of 66p.
B.F.P.O. and EIRE – 18p for the first book plus 8p per copy for the next 6 books, thereafter 3p per book.
OTHER OVERSEAS CUSTOMERS – 20p for the first book and 10p per copy for each additional book.

Name ....

Address ....

....